G000069910

GLOBULINS

BIOCHEMISTRY, PRODUCTION AND ROLE IN IMMUNITY

PROTEIN BIOCHEMISTRY, SYNTHESIS, STRUCTURE AND CELLULAR FUNCTIONS

Additional books in this series can be found on Nova's website under the Series tab.

Additional e-books in this series can be found on Nova's website under the e-book tab.

PROTEIN BIOCHEMISTRY, SYNTHESIS, STRUCTURE AND CELLULAR FUNCTIONS

GLOBULINS

BIOCHEMISTRY, PRODUCTION AND ROLE IN IMMUNITY

SHEILA D. MILFORD
EDITOR

New York

For permission to use material from this book please contact us:
Telephone 631-231-7269; Fax 631-231-8175
Web Site: http://www.novapublishers.com

NOTICE TO THE READER

The Publisher has taken reasonable care in the preparation of this book, but makes no expressed or implied warranty of any kind and assumes no responsibility for any errors or omissions. No liability is assumed for incidental or consequential damages in connection with or arising out of information contained in this book. The Publisher shall not be liable for any special, consequential, or exemplary damages resulting, in whole or in part, from the readers' use of, or reliance upon, this material. Any parts of this book based on government reports are so indicated and copyright is claimed for those parts to the extent applicable to compilations of such works.

Independent verification should be sought for any data, advice or recommendations contained in this book. In addition, no responsibility is assumed by the publisher for any injury and/or damage to persons or property arising from any methods, products, instructions, ideas or otherwise contained in this publication.

This publication is designed to provide accurate and authoritative information with regard to the subject matter covered herein. It is sold with the clear understanding that the Publisher is not engaged in rendering legal or any other professional services. If legal or any other expert assistance is required, the services of a competent person should be sought. FROM A DECLARATION OF PARTICIPANTS JOINTLY ADOPTED BY A COMMITTEE OF THE AMERICAN BAR ASSOCIATION AND A COMMITTEE OF PUBLISHERS.

Additional color graphics may be available in the e-book version of this book.

Library of Congress Cataloging-in-Publication Data

ISBN: 978-1-63117-781-1
LCCN: 2014936827

Published by Nova Science Publishers, Inc. † New York

CONTENTS

Preface   **vii**

Chapter 1   The Role of Immunoglobulins in Monoclonal
                 Gammopathies   **1**
                 Maria Gkotzamanidou and Evangelos Terpos

Chapter 2   The Role of Immunoglobulins in Anaphylaxis   **29**
                 Luca Roncati and Giuseppe Barbolini

Chapter 3   Biochemical Characteristics, and Nutraceutical
                 and Technological Uses of Amaranth Globulins   **41**
                 *Oliviert Martínez-Cruz, Francisco Cabrera-Chávez
                 and Octavio Paredes-López*

Chapter 4   Seed Storage Globulins: Their Descent from Bacterial
                 Ancestors and Mechanisms of Degradation   **71**
                 Andrei D. Shutov and Karl A. Wilson

Index   **105**

PREFACE

Globulins are plasma proteins mostly synthesized by liver and lymphatic tissues. They fall into α-globulins (antiprotease / protease globulins), β-globulins (carrier globulins) and γ-globulin (immuno globulins). More in particular, an immuno globulin is a serum glycoprotein with an Y-shaped quaternary structure, secreted by activated plasma cells in response to a foreign macromolecule. This book discusses the role of immunoglobulins in monoclonal gammopathies; the role of immunoglobulins in anaphylaxis; the biochemical characteristics, and nutraceutical and technological uses of amaranth globulins; and seed storage globulins.

Chapter 1 – Immunoglobulins are glycoproteins, produced by plasma cells in response to an immunogen and function as antibodies; therefore, are of major value for the defense of the host. They derive their name from their characteristic migration as discrete bands when antibody-containing serum is placed in an electrical field.

At the end of 19th century, Dr. Henry Bence Jones observed the high excretion of proteins and their heat properties by precipitating in the presence of nitric acid and re-dissolving them by heat, in patients' urine specimen and thus, heralded the extensive research on the field of monoclonal gammopathies. The monoclonal gammopathies (paraproteinaemias) are a group of disorders associated with monoclonal proliferation of plasma cells within the bone marrow. This group of disorders includes both benign, i.e., monoclonal gammopathy of undetermined significance (MGUS) and malignant disorders such as multiple myeloma. They are characterized by the secretion of electrophoretically and immunologically homogeneous proteins, overproduced by a single clone of cells. Each monoclonal protein (M-protein or paraprotein) consists of two heavy polypeptide chains of the same isotype and two light polypeptide chains of the same type. The heavy polypeptide chains are IgG, IgA, IgM, IgD and IgE, while the light chain types are kappa (k) and lambda (λ).

The detection of monoclonal immunoglobulins with serum and urine protein agarose gel electrophoresis or capillary zone electrophoresis has been the reference diagnostic method for the monoclonal gammopathies. The identification of isotype of monoclonal protein by performing immunofixation has been widespread used with further applications in the identification of the type of cryoglobulins, as well. The detection of monoclonal immunoglobulin free light chains (FLCs) in the serum has been introduced in early 2000, and since then has contributed significantly in the diagnosis, prognosis and follow up of the patients with monoclonal gammopathies, especially for those with non secretory and oligosecretory myeloma or amyloidosis. Novel heavy/light chain assays have been recently introduced in the diagnosis and follow-up of specific monoclonal gammopathies such as oligosecretory myeloma.

Moreover, immunoglobulins have implicated in the treatment and prevention of monoclonal gammopathies; the current translational research focus in the field is on development of immune strategies, i.e., vaccines and adoptive immunotherapy and more effective immunoglobulin-based therapies.

In the present chapter the authors discuss the utility of immunoglobulins in the diagnosis, prognosis and monitoring of treatment efficacy of patients with monoclonal gammopathies. In addition, they will discuss about possible technical pitfalls inherent to each technique. The authors focus on multiple myeloma, monoclonal gammopathy of undetermined significance, macroglobulinaimia Waldenström, AL amyloidosis and light chain deposition disease and they conclude all the current data and the prospectives of immunoglobulins in the treatment and pathogenesis of these monoclonal gammopathies.

Chapter 2 – The globulins are plasma proteins mostly synthesized by liver and lymphatic tissues. They fall into α-globulins (antiprotease/protease globulins), β-globulins (carrier globulins) and γ-globulin (immunoglobulins). More in particular, an immuno globulin is a serum glycoprotein with a Y-shaped quaternary structure, secreted by plasma cells in response to a foreign macromolecule. The symmetrical structure of an immunoglobulin consists of a central stem and two side arms, made up of two light (L) chains and two heavy (H) chains, covalently linked by disulfide bridges on cysteine residues. Both the heavy and light chains are formed by an aminoterminal variable region (V) and a carboxyterminal constant region (C). The variable regions of a heavy chain (VH) and of a light chain (VL) form the binding site for the antigen. The differences in the aminoacid sequence of the constant regions confer to the immunoglobulins a distinction in classes (isotypes). Five types of heavy chains (α, δ, ε, γ, μ) give rise to five different classes of immunoglobulis, known as IgA, IgD, IgE, IgG and IgM. Among these, IgE and IgG4 play a key role in allergic reactions. The term anaphylaxis refers to a severe whole-body allergic response, against a foreign substance denominated allergen, which, if not promptly treated, can lead to the patient's death. The authors' research group has found that the spleen can be considered the human shock organ, given its closed circulation related to the periodic shutdown of the blood in the red pulp sinuses. This is attested by the evidence of activated basophils and degranulated mast cells, stained by Pagoda red, only in the sinuses of patients, who have died from anaphylactic shock.

Chapter 3 – Seed storage proteins have been nutritional and functionally valuable in the food industry and for human consumption. The Osborne's classical technique has been used to extract and classify seed storage proteins; additionally, in the last decades molecular properties have been also used for their characterization. Amaranth proteins, most of them being globulins (salt soluble proteins), have good essential amino acid levels. The nutritional, nutraceutical and technological properties shown by amaranth make it highly attractive to be incorporated into food formulations and to complement or replace some conventional cereal grains. The functional properties of its proteins provide good technological characteristics to food matrices. Several studies have shown that globulins are involved in some immunological processes suggesting that the immune-stimulating effects may lead to B lymphocyte activation and subsequent T cell proliferation *in vitro*. Other bioactive properties have been found in peptides from globulins mainly as outstanding antihypertensive agents. The previous characteristics, plus some others, are showing that the strong potential of amaranth and especially of its globulins should lead both of them to wider food and nutraceutical uses.

Chapter 4 – Legumin and vicilin are seed storage globulins characteristic of spermatophytes. Subunits of both the globulins are composed of homologous N-terminal and C-terminal domains. A β-barrel of eight antiparallel β-strands conjoined with a group of α-helices represents the structural basis of the domains. Legumin and vicilin share tertiary and quaternary structures with homologous bacterial two-domain oxalate decarboxylases that are regarded as the most ancient two-domain progenitors of seed storage globulins. A green alga two-domain protein highly homologous to bacterial oxalate decarboxylases reflects features of the most ancient plant ancestor of seed storage globulins. The diversification of the storage globulin evolutionary pathway into legumin and vicilin branches occurred at the level of non-seed plants like club moss and fern. The development of legumin/vicilin-like proteins into spermatophyte legumin and vicilin consisted of insertion of hydrophilic sequence regions specifically extended inside the domain structures of genuine storage globulins. These extensions are regarded as specific targets for immediate proteolytic attack in legumin and vicilin structures.

Two distinct mechanisms of proteolysis are responsible for the degradation of seed storage globulins in germinating seeds and *in vitro*, limited and extensive (one-by-one) proteolyses. The limited proteolysis is restricted to cleavage of a limited number of peptide bonds specifically susceptible to proteolytic attack. In contrast, the extensive proteolysis is unlimited and consists of one-by-one deep degradation of protein molecules. The separate analysis of the kinetics of limited and extensive proteolyses *in vitro* detected two pathways of degradation of seed storage globulins. In the first, exclusively limited proteolysis occurs at the beginning of the reaction when the native protein substrate is inaccessible to one-by-one proteolysis. In this case, structural alterations of the protein substrate due to the limited proteolysis are expected to bring about its susceptibility to unlimited degradation by the one-by-one mechanism. In the second pathway, the packing density of a storage globulin molecule is relatively low, resulting in susceptibility of the native protein substrate to one-by-one proteolysis. In this case limited and one-by-one proteolyses occur in parallel independent of each other from the very beginning of the reaction. On the basis of comparison of the patterns of *in vitro* and *in vivo* proteolysis it was suggested that both the pathways of massive storage globulin degradation do occur during germination and seedling growth.

In: Globulins
Editor: Sheila D. Milford

ISBN: 978-1-63117-781-1
© 2014 Nova Science Publishers, Inc.

Chapter 1

THE ROLE OF IMMUNOGLOBULINS IN MONOCLONAL GAMMOPATHIES

Maria Gkotzamanidou, M.D., Ph.D.[*1]
and Evangelos Terpos, M.D.[2]

[1]LeBow Institute for Myeloma Therapeutics and Jerome Lipper Multiple
Myeloma Center, Department of Medical Oncology,
Dana-Farber Cancer Institute, Harvard Medical School, Boston, MA, US
[2]Department of Clinical Therapeutics, National and Kapodistrian
University of Athens, School of Medicine, Alexandra General Hospital,
Athens, Greece

ABSTRACT

Immunoglobulins are glycoproteins, produced by plasma cells in
response to an immunogen and function as antibodies; therefore, are of
major value for the defense of the host. They derive their name from their
characteristic migration as discrete bands when antibody-containing
serum is placed in an electrical field.

At the end of 19th century, Dr. Henry Bence Jones observed the high
excretion of proteins and their heat properties by precipitating in the

* Correspondence: Dr. Maria Gkotzamanidou, LeBow Institute for Myeloma Therapeutics and
Jerome Lipper Multiple Myeloma Center, Department of Medical Oncology, Dana-Farber
Cancer Institute, Harvard Medical School, M551, 450 Brookline Avenue, 02215, Boston,
MA, US, Tel. +1 617460-0022, Fax. +1 617632-2140, E-mail: maria_gkotzamanidou
@dfci.harvard.edu.

presence of nitric acid and re-dissolving them by heat, in patients' urine specimen and thus, heralded the extensive research on the field of monoclonal gammopathies. The monoclonal gammopathies (paraproteinaemias) are a group of disorders associated with monoclonal proliferation of plasma cells within the bone marrow. This group of disorders includes both benign, i.e., monoclonal gammopathy of undetermined significance (MGUS) and malignant disorders such as multiple myeloma. They are characterized by the secretion of electrophoretically and immunologically homogeneous proteins, overproduced by a single clone of cells. Each monoclonal protein (M-protein or paraprotein) consists of two heavy polypeptide chains of the same isotype and two light polypeptide chains of the same type. The heavy polypeptide chains are IgG, IgA, IgM, IgD and IgE, while the light chain types are kappa (k) and lambda (λ).

The detection of monoclonal immunoglobulins with serum and urine protein agarose gel electrophoresis or capillary zone electrophoresis has been the reference diagnostic method for the monoclonal gammopathies. The identification of isotype of monoclonal protein by performing immunofixation has been widespread used with further applications in the identification of the type of cryoglobulins, as well. The detection of monoclonal immunoglobulin free light chains (FLCs) in the serum has been introduced in early 2000, and since then has contributed significantly in the diagnosis, prognosis and follow up of the patients with monoclonal gammopathies, especially for those with non secretory and oligosecretory myeloma or amyloidosis. Novel heavy/light chain assays have been recently introduced in the diagnosis and follow-up of specific monoclonal gammopathies such as oligosecretory myeloma.

Moreover, immunoglobulins have implicated in the treatment and prevention of monoclonal gammopathies; the current translational research focus in the field is on development of immune strategies i.e. vaccines and adoptive immunotherapy and more effective immunoglobulin-based therapies.

In the present chapter we discuss the utility of immunoglobulins in the diagnosis, prognosis and monitoring of treatment efficacy of patients with monoclonal gammopathies. In addition, we will discuss about possible technical pitfalls inherent to each technique. We focus on multiple myeloma, monoclonal gammopathy of undetermined significance, macroglobulinaimia Waldenström, AL amyloidosis and light chain deposition disease and we conclude all the current data and the prospectives of immunoglobulins in the treatment and pathogenesis of these monoclonal gammopathies.

INTRODUCTION

The first report of existence of Immunoglobulins (Igs) was in late 1800s, when Emil von Behring and Shibasaburo Kitasato reported the existence of an agent in the blood that could neutralize diphtheria toxin. The following year, the term "Antikörper" was introduced to describe this finding.

Over the past century, the investigation into the structure and function has shed light on the magnificent diversity, complex nature and multifunctional roles of Igs.

Igs mainly serve as cell-surface receptors for antigen which permit cell signaling and cell activation and also, as soluble effector molecules that individually bind and neutralize remote antigens.

However, aberrant function of Igs or impairment of B-cells immunity, i.e., mature B-cells and plasma cells which produce Igs are implicated in autoimmune disorders, infections and carcinogenesis. Monoclonal gammopathies are a group of disorders characterized by a single clone of cells within B lineage that produce the Monoclonal protein (paraprotein, or M-protein). Both benign such as MGUS and neoplasias, i.e., MM are included in this group of diseases. They are characterized by the secretion of electrophoretically and immunologically homogeneous proteins, overproduced by a single clone of cells. Each M-protein consists of two heavy polypeptide chains of the same isotype and two light polypeptide chains of the same type. Here, we focus on the role of Igs in the pathogenesis and treatment of monoclonal gammopathies. Moreover, we discuss the implication of monoclonal Igs in the diagnosis, monitoring and prognosis of patients with monoclonal gammopathies.

PRODUCTION

Immunoglobulines (Igs) or antibodies (Abs) are complex proteins synthesized by B-lineage immune cells (mature B- lymphocytes and plasma cells) and consist the central elements of humoral immunity and protection against a variety of pathogens [1]. In humans, it has been estimated that lymphocytes can produce approximately 10^{15} antibodies of different specifities [2-4].

Early B-cell development is characterized by the recombination of IgH (heavy) and IgL (light) chain loci to generate a functional B-cell antigen receptor (BCR), and Igs themselves play an important role in regulating B-cell development [5-6]. B-cell development begins in the fetal liver and consequently, takes place in bone marrow. Pre-B cells arise from progenitor (pro-B) cells which do not express surface Ig nor BCR. The rearrangement of the IgH locus is initiated at the pro-B cell or from the lymphocytes progenitors and leads to production of Igμ chain. Igμ chain is expressed on the surface of the large pre-B-cells in the form of the pre-BCR. Pre-BCR mediated signaling can serve as proliferative stimulus and therefore, expand pre-B cells with functional recombined Igμ (Figure 1).

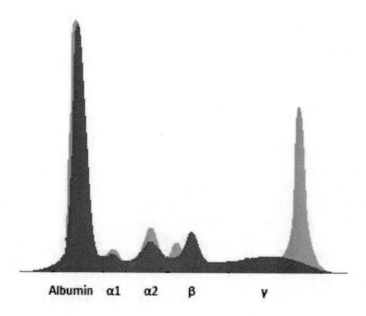

Figure 1. SPEP of healthy donor (blue) and patient with MM (red).

In frame IgL gene rearrangements in small pre-B cells result in the expression of a BCR that is composed of the Igμ H chains and a heterodimer of proteins termed surrogate L chains (SLCs), consisting of 2 distinct proteins originally designated Vpre5 and λ5. These immature B cells are subjected to selection processes and eventually enter the pool of long-living mature B cells.

Rearrangements of the variable (V), diversity (D), and joining (J) regions of Ig H-chain, with the V and J regions rearrangements of the Ig L-chain gene segments generate a B-cell repertoire expressing antibodies capable of recognizing many different antigens.

According to the rearrangement of the H-chain and L-chain gene segments, 3 developmental stages are defined. In the first stage, pro–B cells rearrange the D and J segments of the H-chain, followed by a second rearrangement joining an upstream V region to the rearranged DJ segment.

Subsequently, antigen-driven stimulation through the B-cell antigen receptor and CD40 of naïve B-cells lead them to germinal-center (GC) microenvironment [7]. In the GC the B-cells begin to proliferate and undergo clonal expansion and furthermore, the class switch recombination (CSR) at the IgH locus, somatic hypermutation (SHM) of the IgV regions that encode the antigen-binding site, and the selection for increased affinity of a BCR for its unique antigenic epitope through affinity maturation take place within the GC [8]. During SHM which occurs at a rate much higher than in housekeeping genes, results in diversification of the Ig V repertoire. Concurrently, the Ig constant regions undergo CSR, whereby different subclasses of antibodies (IgG, IgA or IgE) are produced. SHM and CSR that will be discussed further in details, occur in the centroblast stage of B-cell maturation and together are responsible for generating high-affinity antibodies of different subclasses (Table 1) that are capable of mediating specific immune responses. Centroblasts that produce high-affinity antibodies either differentiate into plasma cells that are programmed to secrete large quantities of specific antibodies or become memory B cells that are programmed respond robustly following a second encounter with the same antigen, by quickly differentiating into plasma cells [9].

Table.1. Classes and subclasses of human Igs

Class	IgG	IgA	IgM	IgE	IgD
Subclasses	IgG1 IgG2 IgG3 IgG4	IgA1 IgA2			

STRUCTURE AND FUNCTION OF IMMUNOGLOBULINS

Each Ig is composed of two identical heavy (H)-(50-70 KDa), and two identical light (L)-chains (23KDa) which are connected by disulfide bridges and by non-covalent interactions. Moreover, there are intra-chain disulfide bonds within each of the polypeptide chains. The N-terminal portions of Hand L-chains contain variable domains that bind antigen (Fab fragment), through six hypervariable complementary determining regions. The hinge region constitutes the the region at which the arms of immunoglobulin forms a Y and exhibits some flexibility [5, 10].

Specifically, the L chains contain one variable and one constant region, whereas the H chains are composed of three (IgG, IgA, IgD) or four (IgM and IgE) constant regions that constitute the C-terminal Fc-fragments. The sequence of the constant region of the L-chains defines two types (k and Lambda) which occur in a proportion 2:1 within the Ig repertoire.

IgG comprise four subclasses (IgG1, IgG2, IgG3 and IgG4) and IgA two subclasses (IgA1 and IgA2) (Table 1). Ig chains are glycoproteins, which contain 3–13% carbohydrate depending on the class of the antibody.

Each type of antibody can be produced as a membrane bound protein functioning as a B-cell receptor, or as a secreted protein, which are notably found in serum. The main function of the Fab fragment of the immunoglobulins is the binding of antigenic epitopes via hypervariable (HRV) or complimentarity determining regions (CDRs), while it does not mediate the effector functions of Igs. Igs with different specificities exhibit different CDRs while Igs with identical specificity have the same CDRs. Furthermore, the Fc fragments have multiple functions such as the receptor-mediated phagocytosis (IgG1, IgG3, IgA), cytotoxicity (IgG1, IgG3), stimulation of NK cells (IgG1, IgG3), receptor-mediated transfer via placenta (IgM) and mucosa (IgM, IgA), sensitization of mast cells and basophils (IgE, IgG3) and more.

DIVERSITY OF ANTIBODIES

VDJ Recombination

The mammalian immune system is remarkable for its ability to respond to almost any antigen that exposed to because of the incredible diversity of lymphocyte receptor molecules. This diversity of Abs is generated by various mechanisms which are implicated both in Igs-dependent and –independent stages of lymphocyte development. The H-chains are encoded by recombined VDJ genes that are formed from sets of Variable (V), Diversity (D), and Joining (J) genes, while VJ rearrangements of k and λ chains V genes and J genes encode the L-chains [1, 11]. TCR b-chains and d-chains are similarly encoded by distinct sets of V, D, and J genes, while a- and g-chains are encoded by additional sets of V and J genes.

Expression of lymphocyte-specific RAG1 and RAG2 recombinases leads to the sequential somatic rearrangement of V, D and J gene segments. RAG binds to highly conserved heptamer sequence (e.g., CACAGTG) and to a less well-conserved nine base pair, or nonamer signal sequence (e.g., ACAAAACCC) which is separated by the first one by either a 12- or 23-base-pair spacer (RSSs) and flank each of the V, D, and J gene segments. Both RAG1 and RAG2 proteins, constitute the recombinase that binds to two segments, and forms a synapse prior to the induction of double strand breaks (DSBs) and this gain and loss of nuclotides at the jucntions results in the large and diverse spectrum of Abs [12]. Moreover, RAG plays a role after cleavage by holding the four broken ends together in a RAG post cleavage complex, which is repaired by ubiquitously expressed components of a DNA repair process, known as nonhomologous end-joining (NHEJ) [13-14]. The NHEJ process creates precise joins between the RSS ends, and imprecise joins of the coding ends. NHEJ components involved in V(D)J recombination are Ku70, Ku80, DNA-PKcs, Artemis, XRCC4, and ligase IV.

CLASS SWITCH RECOMBINATION

The constant region of IgH gene (9 functional constant of H-chain genes, hereafter as CH), consists of a series of exons, each of them encoding a separate domain, hinge or terminus. This mechanism termed Class Switch Recombination (CSR), is a deletional recombination, with all these genes undergoing alternative splicing to generate two different types of carboxy-termini. These termini can be either a membrane terminus that anchors Ig on the B lymphocyte surface or a secreted terminus that occurs in the soluble form of the Ig. CSR occurs between highly repetitive and specific sequences termed switch (S) regions.

CSR occurs via introduction of DSBs into the upstream donor Sl and a downstream acceptor S region, and is completed by joining the two broken S regions to each other. CSR also initiated by AID. However, the DNA DSBs are obligate intermediates during this mechanism.

During CSR between the Cμ switch region and one of the switch regions of the rest CH, the same VDJ H-chain variable domain can be juxtaposed to any of the H chain classes, leading to alterad Ab effector function but maintaining the antigen-affinity specificity (receptor function).

SOMATIC HYPERMUTATION

After exposure of B cells to antigen, the Somatic hypermutation (SHM) is activated. SHM plays an important role in Ab diversity and affinity maturation.

The immunoglobulin V genes of GC lymphocytes undergo this mutational procedure at a rate up to 10^3 changes per bp per generation [15-16]. Two different mechanisms are involved into SHM. The first mechanism targets mutation-prone sites that exhibit the RGYW motif, while the second one leads to a nucleotide mismatch between the newly synthesized, the mutated DNA strand and its template partner. AID (Activation-Induced Cytidine Deaminase) induces random mutation in the variable Ig gene segments. After several rounds of mutations and selection, only the colones that express a mutated and with higher affinity Ab will leave the GC and be differentiated to plasma cells.

ACTIVATION-INDUCED CYTIDINE DEAMINASE (AID)

As we described above, SHM and CSR rely entirely on the cytidine deaminase AID to generate deoxycytidine-to-deoxyuridine (C-to-U) mutations in the V region of the immunoglobulin gene during SHM and in the C region of the immunoglobulin H-chain locus during CSR. AID is a single strand DNA (ssDNA) cytidine deaminase that can be expressed in activated GS B cells. Mice and humans with mutated AID exhibit aberrant SHM and CSR and develop hyper-IgM syndrome [17-18]. In a phosporylation-dependent manner, AID amplifies the generation of DSBs. It has been shown recently that there is a link between the function of AID and the formation of DSBs through the phosphorylation [19] of the serine residue at position 38 of AID that is necessary for the formation of DSBs during CSR and also, is induced by the formation of DSBs.

AID converts cytosine into uracil in single-stranded DNA (ssDNA) upstream of the CH1 domain, which in turn, causes the formation, of uracil-guanine mismatched DNA base pairs. The deamination by AID occurs in highly repetitive switch regions.

The base excision repair protein uracil DNA glycosylase (UNG) removes the mismatched uracil base, creating an abasic site, while differential repair of this lesion leads to either SHM with formation of transitions or transversions or CSR, with formation of DNA DSBs at the constant genes.

AID function is of high importance for the Abs diversification in B cells through SHM or CSR and it is now evidenced that AID activity is regulated by posttranslational modifications and also, by interacting proteins [20-21]. AID-mediated mechanisms SHM and CSR contribute significantly in production of a great variety of Abs with wide-ranging specifities and effector functions to response to a limitless repertoire of antigens [22].

MONOCLONAL GAMMOPATHIES

Multiple Myeloma

The discovery of the entity of monoclonal gammopathies took place at the end of 19th century, when Dr. Bence Jones observed in urine samples of patients an abnormal substance which was precipitating in the presence of nitric acid, re-dissolving by heating and again precipitating by cooling [23-24]. Later, this substance was identified as immunoglobulin and its presence was attributed to multiple myeloma (MM). In the category of disorders that associated with monoclonal immunoglobulinopathies are included the MM, macroglobulinemia Waldenström, AL amyloidosis etc. (Table 2)

Multiple myeloma (MM) is a hematologic malignancy characterized by a multifocal proliferation of clonal, long-lived plasma cells within the bone marrow and associated serum and/or urine monoclonal gammopathy [25]. MM is the most serious and prevalent plasma cell dyscrasia, which accounts for slightly more than 10% of all hematologic cancers [26]. In 2012, an estimated 21,700 newly diagnosed cases of multiple myeloma and 10,710 estimated deaths by the disease were expected in the United States [27]. Recent data from the USA has found that the mean age at diagnosis of MM is 65.8 and 69.8 years for African Americans and Caucasians, respectively [28]. A study based on more than 77,000 individuals showed that MM in all patients preceded by an age-progressive premalignant condition termed monoclonal gammopathy of undetermined significance (MGUS) [29] and the progression rate of MGUS to MM is of 0.5% to 3% per year [30-32]. There are 2 distinct categories of MGUS: lymphoid or lymphoplasmacytoid and plasma cell MGUS. Approximately 15% of MGUS secrete IgM and have a lymphoid or lyphoplasmacytoid phenotype, while the rest cases secrete IgG,A, light chain, D or E and have a plasma cell phenotype. An also, asymptomatic condition and premalignant stage of MM but with a higher burden of monoclonal plasma cells within the BM, termed smoldering multiple myeloma or asymptomatic

MM (SMM) is recognized. SMM is characterized also by absence of symptoms. IMWG diagnostic criteria established SMM as serum M-protein ≥3 g/dL and/or clonal plasma cell population in BM ≥ 10% and lack of end-organ damage (CRAB criteria). Based on retrospective data from the Mayo Clinic, the risk of progression from SMM to MM is 10% per year for the first 5 years, 3% per year for the next 5 years, and 1% for the subsequent 10 years (Table 3).

THE ROLE OF IMMUNOGLOBULINS IN THE DIAGNOSIS OF MM

MM is characterized by the expansion of monoclonal long-lived plasma cells in the bone marrow microenvironment. This plasmacellular population produces monoclonal immunoglobulins. In all cases, plasma cells produce at least a light chain (k more frequently) and frequently a H chain (IgG, IgA, IgD or IgE). IgD 2%. The majority of the MM patients have elevated IgG, 20% IgA and 5-10% only light chains. About 2% will have IgD, while IgE MM is very rare with approximately 50 cases reported in the literature. A double monoclonal component (MC) detected in the serum and/or urine represents a very rare occurrence (2–6% of monoclonal gammopathies).

The H-chain is secreted from the plasma cells into the BM interstitial fluid and ultimately reaches the circulation and allows for diagnosis and monitoring for response to treatment.

The gold standard of diagnosis and monitoring of patients with monoclonal gammopathies remains the serum protein electrophoresis. The Serum agarose electrophoresis (SPEP) estimates the monoclonal Ig that appears as a discrete band on the electrophoretic strip, or as a discrete and high spike on the densitometer tracing, based on their physical properties. The net charge (positive or negative) and the size and shape of the protein commonly are used in differentiating various serum proteins.

The proteins are stained by using a protein dye and their densities are calculated electronically to provide graphical data on the absolute and relative amounts of the various proteins.

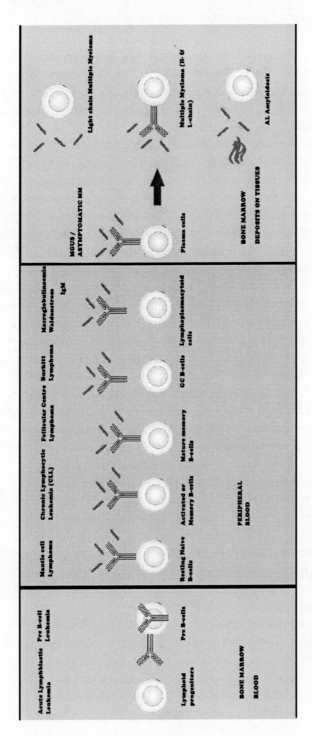

Figure 2. B-cell lineage and associated disorders.

In serum of peripheral blood we identify two major protein groups, the albumin and globulins. Both albumin and globulins carry substances through the bloodstream. During SPEP, these two groups can be separated into five smaller groups (fractions): Albumin, Alpha-1 globulin, Alpha-2 globulin, Beta globulin and Gamma globulins (Figure 2).

Each of these five protein groups moves at a different rate in an electrical field and together form a specific pattern. The pattern of serum protein electrophoresis results depends on the fractions of those two major types of protein. The major protein component of serum, albumin is produced by the liver under normal physiologic conditions. Globulins comprise a much smaller fraction of the total serum protein content. The subsets of these proteins and their relative quantity are the primary focus of the interpretation of SPEP in patients with monoclonal gammopathies.

Albumin, the largest peak, lies closest to the positive electrode. The next five components (globulins) are labeled alpha1, alpha2, beta1, beta2, and gamma. The peaks for these components lie toward the negative electrode, with the gamma peak being closest to that electrode. The albumin band represents the largest protein component of human serum. The albumin level is decreased under circumstances in which there is less production of the protein by the liver or in which there is increased loss or degradation of this protein. Malnutrition, significant liver disease, renal loss (e.g., in nephrotic syndrome), hormone therapy, and pregnancy may account for a low albumin level. Burns also may result in a low albumin level. Levels of albumin are increased in patients with a relative reduction in serum water (e.g., dehydration).

The beta fraction has two peaks labeled beta1 and beta2. Beta1 is composed mostly of transferrin, and beta2 contains beta-lipoprotein. IgA, IgM, and sometimes IgG, along with complement proteins, also can be identified in the beta fraction. Much of the clinical interest is focused on the gamma region of the serum protein spectrum because Igs migrate to this region. Notably, Igs in patients with monoclonal gammopathies often can be found throughout the electrophoretic spectrum. C-reactive protein (CRP) is located in the area between the beta and gamma components.

Close to the negative electrode, the next peaks involve the alpha 1 and alpha 2 components. The alpha1-protein fraction is comprised of alpha1-antitrypsin, thyroid-binding globulin, and transcortin. Malignancy and acute inflammation (resulting from acute-phase reactants) can increase the alpha1-protein band. A decreased alpha1-protein band may occur because of alpha1-antitrypsin deficiency or decreased production of the globulin as a result of liver disease. The alpha-2 band consists also of ceruloplasmin, alpha2-

macroglobulin, and haptoglobin. The alpha2 component is increased as an acute-phase reactant.

Table 2. Criteria for diagnosis of MM, MGUS and SMM

Multiple Myeloma	Monoclonal gammopathy of undetermined significance (MGUS)	Smoldering or Asymptomatic Multiple Myeloma (SMM)
Clonal bone marrow plasma cells ≥ 10%	Clonal bone marrow plasma cells <10% AND	Clonal bone marrow plasma cells ≥10% AND/OR
Presence of serum and/or urinary monoclonal protein (except in patients with true non-secretory MM)	Serum monoclonal protein <3 g/100 ml AND	Serum monoclonal protein (IgG or IgA) ≥3 g/100 ml AND
Evidence of end-organ damage that can be attributed to the underlying plasma cell proliferative disorder, specifically (CRAB): C : Hypercalcemia: serum calcium ≥ 11.5 mg/dl or R : Renal insufficiency, serum creatinine >1.73 mmol/l) A : Anemia, normochromic, normocytic with a hemoglobin value of >2 g/100 ml below the lower limit of normal or a hemoglobin value <10 g/100 ml B : Bone lytic lesions, severe osteopenia or pathologic fractures	Absence of end-organ damage such as hypercalcemia, renal insufficiency, anemia and bone lesions (CRAB) that can be attributed to the plasma cell proliferative disorder	Absence of end-organ damage such as lytic bone lesions, anemia, hypercalcemia or renal failure that can be attributed to a plasma cell proliferative disorder

The quantification of Igs by immunonephelometry (NEPH) relies on the light scatter generated by the binding of H-chain specific antisera. It has been shown [33] these two methods might have inconsistent results, due to protein stains and immune reagents reacting differently to specific monoclonal protein amino acid sequences, and therefore might result in clone-specific variation in staining and antibody binding [33-34]. Further separation of protein subtypes is achieved by performing serum immunofixation electrophoresis (IFE). This method is 10 times more sensitive that SPEP in detection of Igs, and especially of FLCs. To date, IFE is included in the standard diagnostic panel of tests for MM patients in order to detect the specific type of monoclonal chain.

The Capillary zone electrophoresis (CZE) is less frequently used in laboratories for serum protein separation. CZE is able to detect most monoclonal Igs. However, it has been shown that this method fails to detect monoclonal Igs in 5% of MM patients.

CLINICAL PREDICTORS OF PROGRESSION

The serum FLC assay has main application in diagnosis, prognosis and responsiveness of patients with monoclonal gammopathies. First, it has prognostic value in MM, MGUS, SMM and solitary plasmacytoma. Moreover, serum FLCs can be used in conjunction with SPEP and IFE during diagnostic workout for the presence or absence of a monoclonal plasma cell disorder such as MM [35].

The evaluation of 24h urine total protein in combination with performance of urine protein electrophoresis and IFE are necessary tests after the final diagnosis of MM.

Furthermore, the evaluation of FLCs according the International Myeloma Working Group Uniform Response Criteria [36] is a useful tool for the monitoring of the non-measurable disease of patients with non-secretory or oligo-secretory MM and their responsiveness to treatment. The measurable disease is defined by at least one of the 3 following measurements: a. serum monoclonal (M) protein ≥ 1 g/dl b. urine M protein ≥ 200 mg per 24 h or c. involved FLC≥ 10 mg/dl, provided the FLC ratio is abnormal.

To date, the FLCs ratio in serum is one of the most used clinical biomarkers in premalignant conditions of MGUS and SMM [37-38]. Recently, risk stratification schemes for SMM have emerged utilizing methods such as serum M protein and serum FCL ratio [39-40]. Dispenzieri et al. showed that the abnormal κ/λ FLC ratio of ≤ 0.125 or ≥ 8 had a prognostic value for SMM patients and it was independent factor of other risk factors on multivariate analysis [39]. The prognostic value of abnormal FLCs ratio in SMM has been showed also by other groups [41]. Moreover, the sFLC ratio may be a good prognostic marker for determining which patients with high-risk SMM will receive the greatest benefit from early treatment, however, there is no consensus for early initiation of treatment for these patients [42-43].

Futhermore, Rajkumar et al demonstrated that MGUS patients with an abnormal sFLC ratio (defined as ≤ 0.26 or ≥ 1.65) and a high serum M-protein level (1.5 g/dL) had a 58% absolute risk of disease progression after 20 years, whereas MGUS patients with 1 risk factors had only a 21% and 5% absolute risk of disease progression, respectively [44].

THE ROLE OF IMMUNOGLOBULINS IN TREATMENT OF MONOCLONAL GAMMOPATHIES

Multiple Myeloma

The immune system plays an important role in pathogenesis, as well as in treatment of MM, as evidenced by durable responses following allogeneic transplantation. Immunotherapy is a promising therapeutic approach in treatment of MM. Over the last decades, many potent antigens have been identified on myeloma cells that may be promising targens via humoral- and/or cell- mediated immunotherapeutic strategies, while encouraging results have been demonstrated both pre-clinically and in clinical trials [45]. In the present chapter, we focus only on novel antibodies that have shown anti-myeloma activity pre-clinically and we discuss the impact of modification of humoral immunity in patients with MM.

HUMORAL IMMUNITY WITH MONOCLONAL ANTIBODIES

The development of antibody-based therapeutic strategies for MM has focused on cell surface markers expressed by plasma cells such as CD38, CD138, and the tumor adhesion molecule CS-1.

CD38 antigen is a target of interest in the development of antibody-based therapies for MM, as malignant bone marrow plasma cells strongly express CD38 in their surface. Daratumumab is a human monoclonal antibody that has been shown to effectively kill myeloma cells in vitro and in murine models [46]. It has been recently demonstrated that lenalidomide potently enhances the efficacy of this antibody [47]. Ongoing clinical studies are evaluating the combination of CD38 antibody in combination with already used in the MM treatment agents such as lenalidomide and bortezomib [48].

CS1 a cell surface glycoprotein that is highly expressed in plasma cells isolated from MM patients. Elotuzumab (HuLuc63) a humanized anti-CS1 monoclonal Antibody (mAb) which binds to plasma cells and leads plasma cells to undergo apoptosis through antibody-dependent cellular cytotoxicity

(ADCC) [49]. In addition, elotuzomab inhibits the adhesion of plasma cells to the bone marrow stromal cells [50]. In preclinical studies, Elotuzumab demonstrated synergy with bortezomib and lenalidomide [51]. Elotuzomab is a promising agent both alone which warrants further investigation both alone and in combination therapy.

To date, most clinical studies have evaluated immunotherapy in patients with refractory disease, while immunotherapeutic approaches are most likely to elicit potent immunologic clinical responses in a setting of patients with no impaired cellular and humoral immunity. However, the establishment of antibody-based therapeutic strategies with or without chemotherapeutic agents for MM patients or for prevention of disease progression in patients with high-risk SMM appears very promising research goal.

Table 3. Classification of Monoclonal gammopathies / paraproteinemias

Monoclonal gammopathies/ Paraproteinemias
Multiple Myeloma
Monoclonal gammopathy of undetermined significance (MGUS)
Smoldering or Asymptomatic Multiple Myeloma
Solitary plasmatocytoma
AL amyloidosis
POEMS syndrome
B-cell Non-Hodgkin lymphoma

AMYLOIDOSIS

Amyloidosis is a group of diseases characterized by misfolding of proteins with molecular weight of about 10-15 kDa which acquire this alternative and misfolded state at minimum energy and in turn, aggregate into oligomers and polymers. Interaction of these protein with the extracellular matrix also appears to be important and may be related to preferential deposition of amyloid in some organs or tissues. Around 30 different soluble precursor proteins can aggregate and deposited as insoluble amyloid fibrils. Extracellular deposition of amyloid fibrils in organs and tissues results in tissue infiltration and swelling leading to progressive loss of function of the affected organ. Another constituent of all amyloid is serum amyloid P component (SAP). SAP is a glycoprotein that belongs to the pentraxin family and binds to all types of amyloid in a calcium-dependent way. It is protected against proteolysis and thus makes amyloid fibrils resistant to degradation.

Amyloid deposition can be localized or systemic. Systemic amyloidosis leads to serious signs and deterioration of organs and tissues that amyloid has been deposited.

There are many types of systemic amyloidosis but 4 types are seen most frequently: AL(light chain), AA (inflammation), ATTR (hereditary and old age), and Ab2M (dialysis). In the present chapter we focus on AL amyloidosis which is the most common type and is a low tumor burden plasma cell disorder, characterized by deposition of insoluble fibrils composed of Igs light chains, most often lambda LC. Recently, the term monoclonal gammopathy of renal significance (MGRS) was introduced to distinguish monoclonal gammopathies that result in the development of kidney disease from those that are benign such as MGUS. MGRS is defined by the presence of B cell clones and renal disease, due to deposition of the secreted monoclonal Igs. AL amyloidosis is included in this group of diseases [51].

The clinical manifestations of AL amyloidosis are diverse, such as orthostatic hypotension, cardiomyopathy, hepatomegaly, nephrotic syndrome, renal failure, diarrhea, intestinal pseudoobstruction, peripheral neuropathy, autonomic neuropathy, carpal tunnel syndrome (CTS), bleeding, adrenal dysfunction, goiter, glossomegaly and more [52]. The baseline cardiac involvement and the FLCs hematologic response to therapy determine overall survival of patients with AL amyloidosis. The disease often goes unnoticed until severe symptoms appear relatively late in its course.

Without treatment, AL has a rapid progressive course due to uncontrolled tissue damage.

AL amyloidosis is one-fifth as common as MM with incidence 1 case per 10^5 persons annually. The median age of presentation is 70 years.

In the case of AL amyloidosis, the precursor protein is bone marrow plasma cell derived immunoglobulin light chains, which is quite different from the case of ATTR, wherein the precursor protein—transthyretin—is made in the liver.

The presence of monoclonal Ig in the serum and urine is a common finding and contributes significantly to diagnostic workout.

Common findings in the SPEP of AL patients is a typical nephrotic pattern with elevated A2, low γ fraction and low albumin. AL patients exhibit in the serum IFE some polyclonal Ig in the γ fraction and a small monoclonal λ protein that migrates at the β/γ region.

However, due to high protein background it is very difficult to detect any band by densitometry of the SPEP. Several approaches based on two-dimensional electrophoresis [53-54] and Multidimensional Protein Identification Technology [55] have been developed and keep promise for improvement of disease diagnosis and monitoring.

The demonstration that amyloid deposits are formed by light chains is mandatory before starting treatment for AL amyloidosis. Furthermore, immune-electron microscopy on abdominal fat specimen and organ biopsies is used routinely, where amyloid fibrils are positive stained with Congo red, producing a pathognomonic apple green birefringence (red-to-green dichroism) under polarized light [56-58].

The diagnostic work-up in AL amyloidosis includes serum and urine IFE and bone marrow biopsy for demonstration of monoclonal gammopathy [59]. Recently, FLCs in serum level of was included in the criteria of hematologic responsiveness of AL patients [60-61], while significant decrease of involved FLCs are associated with improved overall survival [62].

Furthermore, the FLCs assay has significantly contributed to diagnosis and monitoring of AL patients [57]. The majority of patients with AL amyloidosis exhibit abnormal FLCs levels and ratio, indicating a key role of Igs in pathogenesis of disease. However, caution needed in the interpretation of FLCs assay, as non-reactivity of individual monoclonal FLCs or effect of their dilution values have been reported [63].

MACROGLOBULINEMIA WALDENSTROM

The World Health Organization (WHO) Classification of Tumours of Haematopoietic and Lymphoid Tissues (2008) defines Waldenström macroglobulinemia (WM) as a low-grade malignancy of the mature B-cells and is characterized by infiltration of the bone marrow by a wide spectrum of lymphoplasmacytoid cells or lyphoplasmacytic cells to fully differentiated plasma cells which produce the IgM [64].

The clinical manifestation of the disease are fatigue, hepatomegaly, lymphadenopathy, splenomegaly, anemia (normochromic/normocytic), and due to high levels of IgM hyperviscosity syndrome, peripheral neuropathy, hemolytic anemia and immune complex vasculitis [65-66].

An abundance of evidence shows that most MW cells have somatic mutations in their Igs genes, suggesting that the MW cells have been selected by antigen in GC at a late stage of their differentiation and on the other hand, highlighting the key roles of Igs in pathogenesis of disease.

The evaluation of tumor burden in MW via performance of paraprotein-based methods such as SPEP, is very important for the evaluation of responsiveness of patients with MW. The determination of IgM is based on same principle of SPEP performed for MM evaluation. However, it should be taken into account that the migration pattern and propensity of IgM to form high-order complex in the serum, might make more difficult the interpretation of the results [64, 67]. Furthermore, after initiation of treatment with monoclonal anti-CD20 antibody rituximab can lead to flare reaction, where IgM levels appear to increase without progression of disease. IFE is more sensitive method for detecting the presence of IgM, however, since it is not quantitative should not replace SPEP.

The changes of IgM levels reflect the alteration in the population of malignant cells [64, 67]. A consensus panel for WM have based the response criteria of the disease on the serum IgM levels [64]. Moreover, the concentration of IgM at diagnosis is independent predictor of progression of IgM MGUS to MW, lymphoma, AL amyloidosis or Chronic Lymphocytic Leukemia, indicating the important role of Igs in disease progressive course [63, 68-70].

LCDD

Light Chain Deposition Disease (LCDD) is a rare plasma cell dyscrasia characterized by systemic deposition of non – amyloid forming fragments of Ig light chains [71-72]. LCDD, along with light- and heavy-chain deposition disease (LHCDD), and heavy-chain deposition disease (HCDD) belong to the Non-amyloidotic monoclonal immunoglobulin deposition diseases, characterized histopathologically by the presence of nodular glomerulo-sclerosis and glomerular and tubular deposition of monoclonal Ig components.

LCDD is more common in men and the median age at diagnosis is 58 years, representing a younger population in compare to patients with multiple myeloma (MM) and amyloidosis.

The disease is associated with a variety of clinical manifestations, depending on the tissue-specific deposition of light chains. The deposits most often contain k type chains (Vk1 and Vk4) without amyloid P component.

The kidney is the most common organ involved; therefore, LCDD is included into the disease group, termed as "Monoclonal gammopathies of renal significance" (MGRS) [51]. Extra-renal involvement, including heart, liver and nervous system is less frequently present in LCDD patients (20%-23%) [73-74]. The clinical presentation of LCDD patients with renal involvement consists of hypertension, high-grade proteinuria, hematuria, and renal insufficiency. Progressive deposition of LCs leads to renal failure, which accounts for the poor prognosis of LCDD patients with median time to end-stage renal disease (ESRD) of 2.7 years and 5-year ESRD-free survival of 37% [73]. Moreover, LCCD is associated in approximately 65% of the cases with MM which negatively impact patient survival; other prognostic factors include age and extra-renal involvement [73].

The diagnostic screening panel for patients suspected of LCDD includes SPEP, kidney biopsy, IFE in serum and urine and serum FLCs. The levels of FLCs and especially the ratio (k/λ) are of high importance for the monitoring of the LCDD patients according IMW guidelines [75]. Abnormal serum FLC ratio is usually found in 88-100% of LCDD patients [76-77].

Given the important role that light chains play in pathogenesis of LCDD, the disease treatment goal is the suppression of light chains production.

DISCUSSION

Igs are the principal operators of the humoral immunity, while impairment of B-cells, the responsible cells for Igs production, play a role in pathogenesis of auto-immune diseases, infections, and malignant transformation. B-cell development and production of Igs has been extensively studied in mice and humans [78-79].

However, over last decades studies on B-cells and combinatorial rearrangements of Ig loci have revealed a much greater heterogeneity in the cellular differentiation and function of Igs that previously appreciated.

Since hematologic malignancies frequently result in the production of monoclonal Igs, it is expected that this group of disorders can be utilized as a good research model. Moreover, major advances in our understanding of diversity of B-cells immunity and Ig repertoire have significantly contributed to better understanding of the diseases biology and design more effective approaches for therapy. In this chapter, we emphasized Igs in monoclonal gammopathies, as important diagnostic tool and key regulators of pathogenesis of these diseases.

To date, the diagnostic work-up panel for patients suspected of monoclonal gammopathies, regarding the evaluation of monoclonal Ig, includes SPEP, IFE of serum and urine, serum FLCs and estimation of 24h total urine protein. Moreover, the laboratory contribution has proven to valuable as well as, to prognosis and monitoring of response of patients with monoclonal gammopathies.

Over the last decade, the majority of laboratories worldwide are able to perform the above diagnostic tests, increasing the diagnostic sensitivity and consequently, facilitating the efforts of physicians to treat their patients.

In monoclonal gammopathies, the precise quantification of monoclonal Ig and its variations during the course of the diseases, discrimination between monoclonal and polyclonal isotype particularly at low concentrations of monoclonal Igs, information about the ratio of clonal and polyclonal plasma cells and about the grade of immunosuppression is of high importance for prognostication, response evaluation and treatment selection.

Furthermore, the Igs have implications in the treatment of monoclonal gammopathies. Recent studies have shed light on the evaluation of B-cells ontogeny and hematologic carcinogenesis, indicating the existence of malignant counterparts that reflect the expansion of subclones and in turn, development of hematologic malignancy. To date, significant efforts have identified a number of potent antigens on malignant plasma cells, and preclinical and clinical studies currently evaluate novel humoral and cell mediated immunotherapeutic strategies for treatment of malignant monoclonal gammopathies (MM, MW).

In addition, in MM and MW the presence of mutation of Ig genes suggest that the origin of these malignant cells is post GC differentiation and antigen stimulation. Chromosomal translocation of Ig loci are also present in many hematologic malignancies [80-81], and NG technology aims to identify the heterogeneity of patients with monoclonal gammopathies. As new data emerge, this knowledge is likely to provide novel targets for developing more effective strategies and biomarkers for better patients stratification but also, for prediction of progression of patients on premalignant stages.

REFERENCES

[1]   Tonegawa S. [*Molecular biology of immunologic recognition*]. Tanpakushitsu Kakusan Koso 1987;32:239-50.
[2]   Ansel KM, Cyster JG. Chemokines in lymphopoiesis and lymphoid organ development. *Curr Opin Immunol* 2001;13:172-9.

[3]   Tonegawa S. Somatic generation of antibody diversity. *Nature* 1983;302:575-81.

[4]   Parkin J, Cohen B. An overview of the immune system. *Lancet* 2001;357:1777-89.

[5]   Mix E, Goertsches R, Zett UK. Immunoglobulins--basic considerations. *J Neurol* 2006;253 Suppl 5:V9-17.

[6]   LeBien TW, Tedder TF. B lymphocytes: how they develop and function. *Blood* 2008;112:1570-80.

[7]   Victora GD, Nussenzweig MC. Germinal centers. *Annu Rev Immunol* 2012;30:429-57.

[8]   Natkunam Y. The biology of the germinal center. *Hematology Am Soc Hematol Educ Program* 2007:210-5.

[9]   McHeyzer-Williams LJ, McHeyzer-Williams MG. Memory B cell evolution: B cell biology. *Adv Exp Med Biol* 2007;596:31-45.

[10] Schroeder HW, Jr., Cavacini L. Structure and function of immunoglobulins. *J Allergy Clin Immunol* 2010;125:S41-52.

[11] Schroeder HW, Jr., Cavacini L. Structure and function of immunoglobulins. *J Allergy Clin Immunol* 2010;125:S41-52.

[12] Sleckman BP. Lymphocyte antigen receptor gene assembly: multiple layers of regulation. *Immunol Res* 2005;32:253-8.

[13] de Villartay JP. V(D)J recombination deficiencies. *Adv Exp Med Biol* 2009;650:46-58.

[14] Schatz DG, Swanson PC. V(D)J recombination: mechanisms of initiation. *Annu Rev Genet* 2011;45:167-202.

[15] McKean D, Huppi K, Bell M, Staudt L, Gerhard W, Weigert M. Generation of antibody diversity in the immune response of BALB/c mice to influenza virus hemagglutinin. *Proc Natl Acad Sci U S A* 1984;81:3180-4.

[16] Berek C, Milstein C. Mutation drift and repertoire shift in the maturation of the immune response. *Immunol Rev* 1987;96:23-41.

[17] Muramatsu M, Kinoshita K, Fagarasan S, Yamada S, Shinkai Y, Honjo T. Class switch recombination and hypermutation require activation-induced cytidine deaminase (AID), a potential RNA editing enzyme. *Cell* 2000;102:553-63.

[18] Revy P, Muto T, Levy Y, et al. Activation-induced cytidine deaminase (AID) deficiency causes the autosomal recessive form of the Hyper-IgM syndrome (HIGM2). *Cell* 2000;102:565-75.

[19] Vuong BQ, Herrick-Reynolds K, Vaidyanathan B, et al. A DNA break- and phosphorylation-dependent positive feedback loop promotes

immunoglobulin class-switch recombination. *Nature immunology* 2013;14:1183-9.

[20] Aoufouchi S, Faili A, Zober C, et al. Proteasomal degradation restricts the nuclear lifespan of AID. *The Journal of experimental medicine* 2008;205:1357-68.

[21] Orthwein A, Patenaude AM, Affar el B, Lamarre A, Young JC, Di Noia JM. Regulation of activation-induced deaminase stability and antibody gene diversification by Hsp90. *The Journal of experimental medicine* 2010;207:2751-65.

[22] Orthwein A, Patenaude AM, Affar el B, Lamarre A, Young JC, Di Noia JM. Regulation of activation-induced deaminase stability and antibody gene diversification by Hsp90. *The Journal of experimental medicine* 2010;207:2751-65.

[23] Bence Jones, H. On a new substance occurring in the urine of a patient with mollities ossium. *Philosophical Transactions of the Royal Society of London (Biology)*, 1848, 55-62.

[24] Kyle RA. Multiple myeloma: an odyssey of discovery. *British journal of haematology* 2000;111:1035-44.

[25] Anderson KC, Carrasco RD. Pathogenesis of myeloma. *Annual review of pathology.* 2011;6:249-74.

[26] Siegel R, Naishadham D, Jemal A. Cancer statistics, 2013. *CA: a cancer journal for clinicians.* 2013 Jan;63(1):11-30.

[27] Raab MS, Podar K, Breitkreutz I, Richardson PG, Anderson KC. Multiple myeloma. *Lancet.* 2009 Jul 25;374(9686):324-39.

[28] Waxman AJ, Mink PJ, Devesa SS, et al. Racial disparities in incidence and outcome in multiple myeloma: a population-based study. *Blood* 2010;116:5501-6.

[29] Landgren O, Kyle RA, Pfeiffer RM, Katzmann JA, Caporaso NE, Hayes RB, et al. Monoclonal gammopathy of undetermined significance (MGUS) consistently precedes multiple myeloma: a prospective study. *Blood.* 2009 May 28;113(22):5412-7.

[30] Weiss BM, Abadie J, Verma P, Howard RS, Kuehl WM. A monoclonal gammopathy precedes multiple myeloma in most patients. *Blood.* 2009 May 28;113(22):5418-22.

[31] Kyle RA, Rajkumar SV. Monoclonal gammopathy of undetermined significance and smouldering multiple myeloma: emphasis on risk factors for progression. *British journal of haematology.* 2007 Dec;139(5):730-43.

[32] Blade J, Rosinol L, Cibeira MT, de Larrea CF. Pathogenesis and progression of monoclonal gammopathy of undetermined significance. *Leukemia*. 2008 Sep;22(9):1651-7.

[33] Murray DL, Ryu E, Snyder MR, Katzmann JA. Quantitation of serum monoclonal proteins: relationship between agarose gel electrophoresis and immunonephelometry. *Clin Chem* 2009;55:1523-9.

[34] Sinclair D, Ballantyne F, Shanley S, Caine E, O'Reilly D, Shenkin A. Estimation of paraproteins by immunoturbidimetry and electrophoresis followed by scanning densitometry. *Ann Clin Biochem* 1990;27 (Pt 4):335-7.

[35] Landgren O, Kyle RA, Rajkumar SV. From myeloma precursor disease to multiple myeloma: new diagnostic concepts and opportunities for early intervention. *Clinical cancer research : an official journal of the American Association for Cancer Research* 2011;17:1243-52.

[36] Kyle RA, Rajkumar SV. Criteria for diagnosis, staging, risk stratification and response assessment of multiple myeloma. *Leukemia* 2009;23:3-9.

[37] Katzmann JA, Clark R, Kyle RA, et al. Suppression of uninvolved immunoglobulins defined by heavy/light chain pair suppression is a risk factor for progression of MGUS. *Leukemia* 2013;27:208-12.

[38] Katzmann JA, Snyder MR, Rajkumar SV, et al. Long-term biological variation of serum protein electrophoresis M-spike, urine M-spike, and monoclonal serum free light chain quantification: implications for monitoring monoclonal gammopathies. *Clinical chemistry* 2011;57:1687-92.

[39] Dispenzieri A, Kyle RA, Katzmann JA, et al. Immunoglobulin free light chain ratio is an independent risk factor for progression of smoldering (asymptomatic) multiple myeloma. *Blood* 2008;111:785-9.

[40] Larsen JT, Kumar SK, Dispenzieri A, Kyle RA, Katzmann JA, Rajkumar SV. Serum free light chain ratio as a biomarker for high-risk smoldering multiple myeloma. *Leukemia* 2013;27:941-6.

[41] Kastritis E, Terpos E, Moulopoulos L, et al. Extensive bone marrow infiltration and abnormal free light chain ratio identifies patients with asymptomatic myeloma at high risk for progression to symptomatic disease. *Leukemia* 2013;27:947-53.

[42] Dispenzieri A, Kumar S. Treatment for high-risk smoldering myeloma. *N Engl J Med* 2013;369:1764.

[43] Dispenzieri A, Stewart AK, Chanan-Khan A, et al. Smoldering multiple myeloma requiring treatment: time for a new definition? *Blood* 2013;122:4172-81.

[44] Rajkumar SV, Kyle RA, Therneau TM, et al. Serum free light chain ratio is an independent risk factor for progression in monoclonal gammopathy of undetermined significance. *Blood* 2005;106:812-7.

[45] Rosenblatt J, Bar-Natan M, Munshi NC, Avigan DE. Immunotherapy for multiple myeloma. *Expert Rev Hematol* 2014;7:91-6.

[46] de Weers M, Tai YT, van der Veer MS, et al. Daratumumab, a novel therapeutic human CD38 monoclonal antibody, induces killing of multiple myeloma and other hematological tumors. *J Immunol* 2011;186:1840-8.

[47] van der Veer MS, de Weers M, van Kessel B, et al. Towards effective immunotherapy of myeloma: enhanced elimination of myeloma cells by combination of lenalidomide with the human CD38 monoclonal antibody daratumumab. *Haematologica* 2011;96:284-90.

[48] *http://clinicaltrials.gov/*

[49] Tai YT, Dillon M, Song W, et al. Anti-CS1 humanized monoclonal antibody HuLuc63 inhibits myeloma cell adhesion and induces antibody-dependent cellular cytotoxicity in the bone marrow milieu. *Blood* 2008;112:1329-37.

[50] Hsi ED, Steinle R, Balasa B, et al. CS1, a potential new therapeutic antibody target for the treatment of multiple myeloma. *Clinical cancer research : an official journal of the American Association for Cancer Research* 2008;14:2775-84.

[51] Fermand JP, Bridoux F, Kyle RA, et al. How I treat monoclonal gammopathy of renal significance (MGRS). *Blood* 2013;122:3583-90.

[52] Kyle RA, Gertz MA. Primary systemic amyloidosis: clinical and laboratory features in 474 cases. *Semin Hematol* 1995;32:45-59.

[53] Lavatelli F, Perlman DH, Spencer B, et al. Amyloidogenic and associated proteins in systemic amyloidosis proteome of adipose tissue. *Mol Cell Proteomics* 2008;7:1570-83.

[54] Lavatelli F, Vrana JA. Proteomic typing of amyloid deposits in systemic amyloidoses. *Amyloid* 2011;18:177-82.

[55] Brambilla F, Lavatelli F, Di Silvestre D, et al. Reliable typing of systemic amyloidoses through proteomic analysis of subcutaneous adipose tissue. *Blood* 2012;119:1844-7.

[56] Arbustini E, Verga L, Concardi M, Palladini G, Obici L, Merlini G. Electron and immuno-electron microscopy of abdominal fat identifies and characterizes amyloid fibrils in suspected cardiac amyloidosis. *Amyloid* 2002;9:108-14.

[57] Falk RH, Comenzo RL, Skinner M. The systemic amyloidoses. *N Engl J Med* 1997;337:898-909.

[58] Comenzo RL, Reece D, Palladini G, et al. Consensus guidelines for the conduct and reporting of clinical trials in systemic light-chain amyloidosis. *Leukemia* 2012;26:2317-25.

[59] Lachmann HJ, Gallimore R, Gillmore JD, et al. Outcome in systemic AL amyloidosis in relation to changes in concentration of circulating free immunoglobulin light chains following chemotherapy. *Br J Haematol* 2003;122:78-84.

[60] Kumar S, Dispenzieri A, Lacy MQ, et al. Revised prognostic staging system for light chain amyloidosis incorporating cardiac biomarkers and serum free light chain measurements. *J Clin Oncol* 2012;30:989-95.

[61] Katzmann JA, Abraham RS, Dispenzieri A, Lust JA, Kyle RA. Diagnostic performance of quantitative kappa and lambda free light chain assays in clinical practice. *Clin Chem* 2005;51:878-81.

[62] Palladini G, Dispenzieri A, Gertz MA, et al. New criteria for response to treatment in immunoglobulin light chain amyloidosis based on free light chain measurement and cardiac biomarkers: impact on survival outcomes. *J Clin Oncol* 2012;30:4541-9.

[63] Tate JR, Mollee P, Dimeski G, Carter AC, Gill D. Analytical performance of serum free light-chain assay during monitoring of patients with monoclonal light-chain diseases. *Clin Chim Acta* 2007;376:30-6.

[64] Owen RG, Kyle RA, Stone MJ, et al. Response assessment in Waldenstrom macroglobulinaemia: update from the VIth International Workshop. *Br J Haematol* 2013;160:171-6.

[65] Kyle RA, Therneau TM, Rajkumar SV, et al. Long-term follow-up of IgM monoclonal gammopathy of undetermined significance. *Blood* 2003;102:3759-64.

[66] Gertz MA. Immunoglobulin light chain amyloidosis: 2011 update on diagnosis, risk-stratification, and management. *Am J Hematol* 2011;86:180-6.

[67] Rajkumar SV, Harousseau JL, Durie B, et al. Consensus recommendations for the uniform reporting of clinical trials: report of the International Myeloma Workshop Consensus Panel 1. *Blood* 2011;117:4691-5.

[68] Aoki H, Takishita M, Kosaka M, Saito S. Frequent somatic mutations in D and/or JH segments of Ig gene in Waldenstrom's macroglobulinemia

and chronic lymphocytic leukemia (CLL) with Richter's syndrome but not in common CLL. *Blood* 1995;85:1913-9.

[69]   Wagner SD, Martinelli V, Luzzatto L. Similar patterns of V kappa gene usage but different degrees of somatic mutation in hairy cell leukemia, prolymphocytic leukemia, Waldenstrom's macroglobulinemia, and myeloma. *Blood* 1994;83:3647-53.

[70]   Martin-Jimenez P, Garcia-Sanz R, Balanzategui A, et al. Molecular characterization of heavy chain immunoglobulin gene rearrangements in Waldenstrom's macroglobulinemia and IgM monoclonal gammopathy of undetermined significance. *Haematologica* 2007;92:635-42.

[71]   Randall RE, Williamson WC, Jr., Mullinax F, Tung MY, Still WJ. Manifestations of systemic light chain deposition. *Am J Med.* 1976; 60(2): 293-9.

[72]   Gertz MA. Managing light chain deposition disease. *Leuk Lymphoma.* 2012; 53(2):183-4.

[73]   Pozzi C, D'Amico M, Fogazzi GB, Curioni S, Ferrario F, Pasquali S, Quattrocchio G, Rollino C, Segagni S, Locatelli F: Light chain deposition disease with renal involvement: Clinical characteristics and prognostic factors. *Am J Kidney Dis* 2003;42: 1154-1163.

[74]   Michopoulos S, Petraki K, Petraki C, Dimopoulos MA. Light chain deposition disease of the liver without renal involvement in a patient with multiple myeloma related to liver failure and rapid fatal outcome. *Dig Dis Sci.* 2002; 47(4): 730-4.

[75]   Dispenzieri A, Kyle R, Merlini G, et al. International Myeloma Working Group guidelines for serum-free light chain analysis in multiple myeloma and related disorders. *Leukemia* 2009;23:215-24.

[76]   Katzmann JA, Kyle RA, Benson J, et al. Screening panels for detection of monoclonal gammopathies. *Clin Chem* 2009;55:1517-22.

[77]   Nasr SH, Valeri AM, Cornell LD, et al. Renal monoclonal immunoglobulin deposition disease: a report of 64 patients from a single institution. *Clin J Am Soc Nephrol* 2012;7:231-9.

[78]   Hardy RR, Kincade PW, Dorshkind K. The protean nature of cells in the B lymphocyte lineage. *Immunity* 2007;26:703-14.

[79]   LeBien TW. Fates of human B-cell precursors. *Blood* 2000;96:9-23.

[80]   Dyer MJ. The detection of chromosomal translocations involving the immunoglobulin loci in B-cell malignancies. *Methods Mol Biol* 2013;971:123-33.

[81] Gonzalez D, van der Burg M, Garcia-Sanz R, et al. Immunoglobulin gene rearrangements and the pathogenesis of multiple myeloma. *Blood* 2007;110:3112-21.

In: Globulins
Editor: Sheila D. Milford

ISBN: 978-1-63117-781-1
© 2014 Nova Science Publishers, Inc.

Chapter 2

THE ROLE OF IMMUNOGLOBULINS IN ANAPHYLAXIS

Luca Roncati and Giuseppe Barbolini

Department of Diagnostic and Clinical Medicine and of Public Health,
Section of Pathology, University of Modena and Reggio Emilia,
Modena, Italy

ABSTRACT

The globulins are plasma proteins mostly synthesized by liver and lymphatic tissues. They fall into α-globulins (antiprotease/protease globulins), β-globulins (carrier globulins) and γ-globulin (immunoglobulins). More in particular, an immunoglobulin is a serum glycoprotein with an Y-shaped quaternary structure, secreted by plasma cells in response to a foreign macromolecule. The symmetrical structure of an immunoglobulin consists of a central stem and two side arms, made up of two light (L) chains and two heavy (H) chains, covalently linked by disulfide bridges on cysteine residues. Both the heavy and light chains are formed by an aminoterminal variable region (V) and a carboxyterminal constant region (C). The variable regions of a heavy chain (VH) and of a light chain (VL) form the binding site for the antigen. The differences in the aminoacid sequence of the constant regions confer to the immunoglobulins a distinction in classes (isotypes). Five types of heavy chains (α, δ, ε, γ, μ) give rise to five different classes of immunoglobulis, known as IgA, IgD, IgE, IgG and IgM. Among these, IgE and IgG4 play a key role in allergic reactions. The term anaphylaxis refers to a severe whole-body allergic response, against a foreign substance denominated allergen, which, if not promptly treated, can lead to the patient's death. Our research group has found that the spleen can be considered the human shock organ, given its closed circulation related to the periodic shutdown of the blood in the red pulp sinuses. This is attested by the evidence of activated basophils and degranulated mast cells, stained by Pagoda red, only in the sinuses of patients, who have died from anaphylactic shock.

INTRODUCTION

The globulins are plasma proteins mostly synthesized by liver and lymphatic tissues. They fall into α-globulins (antiprotease/protease globulins), β-globulins (carrier globulins) and γ-globulin (immunoglobulins). More in particular, an immuno globulin is a serum glycoprotein with a Y-shaped quaternary structure, secreted by activated plasma cells in response to a foreign macromolecule. The plasma cells are activated by CD4+ lymphocytes (T-helper). The artwork the 'Angel of the West' by Julian Voss-Andreae (Figure 1) is a stainless steel sculpture based precisely on the antibody structure, disclosed by Eduardo Padlan (1994). Dedicated to Richard Lerner, past president of the Scripps Research Institute, and installed at the entrance to the main building on the Scripps Florida Campus, the sculpture portrays a human immuno globulin positioned within a circle as an angel and resembling the Vitruvian Man (1490) by Leonardo da Vinci.

The immuno globulins are able to specifically bind each synthetic or natural antigen (virus, toxin, bacterium), exactly as made by the T-cell receptor (TCR) and the major histocompatibility complex (MHC). The result of this specific binding is the composition of an immunocomplex. The opsonization process implies, directly, the neutralization or the perforation of an antigen and, indirectly, the activation of complement system or other immune cells, via Fc (Fragment crystallizable) immunoglobulin receptors.

The discovery of humoral immunity dates back to 1890, when Emil von Behring and Shibasaburo Kitasato used the serum of immunized animals to treat diphtheria in some patients. The protein component of this serum was initially called antitoxin, for its action against bacterial toxins. The early studies about the immunoglobulin structure were performed on the blood of immunized subjects. These researches, however, did not lead to relevant conclusions, because focused on polyclonal antibodies. The most important results were achieved by examining monoclonal antibodies, collected from patients with multiple myeloma.

Figure 1. 3D-rendering of the stainless steel sculpture 'Angel of the West' by Julian Voss-Andreae (2008). The artwork depicts a human immunoglobulin, thought as a guardian angel.

IMMUNOGLOBULINS

The symmetrical structure of an immunoglobulin consists of a central stem and two side arms, made up of two light chains and two heavy chains, covalently linked by disulfide bridges on cysteine residues. The position of these residues is variable, according to the antibody type. The immunoglobulins are encoded in three loci arranged on three different chromosomes (heavy chains on chromosome 14, κ-light chains on chromosome 2, λ-light chains on chromosome 22). Each chain contains a series of units made up by about 110 aminoacids, forming a globular structure called *Ig domain*. Specifically, the Ig domain consists of two β-sheets bound together by a disulfide bridge and composed of 3-5 antiparallel tapes connected by loops. This domain is also contained in other proteins that, for its structural presence, are united under the name of *Ig superfamily*. Both the heavy and light chains are formed by an aminoterminal variable region (V) and a carboxyterminal constant region (C). At the level of the above described loops, the variable regions of a heavy chain (VH) and of a light chain (VL) form the binding site for the antigen. The are two binding sites for each immunoglobulin. The variable regions contain the so-called hypervariable regions, that are stretches of polypeptidic chain with great variability in the aminoacid sequence, in order to ensure the highest specificity in the antigen recognition. These same regions also undergo somatic hypermutation, further increasing their binding specificity. The constant regions are constituted by 3 or 4 Ig domains in the heavy chains (CH) and by a single Ig domain in the light chain (CL). They do not participate in antigen recognition, being only involved in the effector functions of the globulin. On the basis of CL aminoacidic sequence, κ-light chains and λ-light chains are distinguished. In humans, the 60% of antibodies expresses κ-light chains, while only the remaining 40% λ-light chains.

The immunoglobulins can be serum-secreted or membrane-bound, depending on CH regions: in fact the membrane-bound immunoglobulins show an α-helix hydrophobic transmembrane part and a positively charged portion inside the cell. The CH regions confer also flexibility to the so-called hinge zone, a zone between the first two domains (CH1 and CH2), allowing a different orientation (up to 90°) of the arms, in order to bind more antigens simultaneously. Moreover, the differences in the CH aminoacid sequence confer to the immunoglobulins a distinction in classes (isotypes). Five types of heavy chains (α, δ, ε, γ, μ) give rise to five different classes of immunoglobulis, known as IgA, IgD, IgE , IgG, and IgM. Some immunoglobulins are further subdivided into subclasses. Among these, *IgE* and *IgG4* play a key role in allergic reactions and for this reason they can be labeled as 'immunoallergic globulins'.

IMMUNOALLERGIC GLOBULINS

The IgE antibodies are composed by a pair of heavy chains and light chains. The light chains are the same as other immunoglobulins and each chain contain two *Ig domains*, one variable and one constant. The heavy chains are instead specific of IgE, being type ε, and each chain contains a variable Ig domain and four constants Ig domains (Figure 2). For this reason, they resemble the μ heavy chains of IgM, also made up of four CH domains, while IgA, IgD and IgG contain only three Ig domains in their heavy chain.

Figure 2. Graphic example of the monomeric IgE structure: the heavy chains (blue) are made up by five Ig domains, one aminoterminal variable (VH) and four constant (CH1, CH2, CH3, CH4), while the light chain (yellow) consist of two Ig domains, one aminoterminal variable (VL) and one constant (CL). The Ig domains are covalently linked by disulfide bridges (red dashes).

The IgG are the most abundant immunoglobulins in serum, constituting about 70-75% of their total amount. In contrast to pentameric IgM, which are synthesized in the earlier stage of immune response, IgG are monomeric antibodies of secondary response, produced following the isotypic switching, and for their small size are able to cross the placental barrier. Moreover, the breast milk contains a lot of IgG (and IgA). The heavy chains γ can be produced in four different subtypes: γ1, γ2, γ3 and γ4. Therefore, IgG are divided into four sub-groups that is IgG1, IgG2, IgG3 and IgG4.

Over the years different receptors for IgE and IgG have been identified. Unlike IgG4, IgE bind the receptor before than the antigen. The IgE-receptors are present on the surface of mast cells, basophils and eosinophils, while the IgG-receptors chiefly on the membrane of macrophages and neutrophils. Each IgE-receptor is composed of four chains: an α chain, a β chain and two γ chains. The α chain includes two Ig domains responsible for binding with IgE. The β chain crosses the cell membrane four times and it has one ITAM (Immunoreceptor Tyrosine-based Activating Motif) domain and two binding sites for Fyn and Lyn proteins in the cytoplasmic region. The γ chains present two ITAM domains and two short N-terminal extracellular region. During the signal transduction phase, Fyn and Lyn proteins phosphorylate the tyrosine residues in the ITAM domains, with subsequent recruitment of Syk family tyrosine kinases on the phosphorylated sequences. This event causes, on the one side, an increase of intracellular calcium and, on the other side, the activation of A2 phospholipase.

ANAPHYLAXIS

The term anaphylaxis refers to a severe whole-body immuno-allergic reaction against a foreign substance denominated allergen, giving rise to immediate hypersensitivity which, if not promptly treated, can lead to the patient's death. The term was coined by Charles Richet in 1902 and it is derived from the Greek words ἀνά (against) and φύλαξις (protection). Richet was awarded the Nobel Prize for Medicine and Physiology for his research into anaphylaxis in 1913. Anaphylaxis causes 500-1,000 deaths every year (2.4 cases per million people) in the United States. Its incidence is 4-5 cases per 100,000 people per year, with a cumulative risk of 0.5-2% over the life. However, the incidence is on the rise, because of increasing aseptic conditions under which the Western infants are made to live. In this regard, the 'hygiene hypothesis' argues that the allergic reactions rising is related to a failure in the T-helper lymphocytes switch process towards the TH1 population, supplanted by the TH2 population, for the lack of an adequate immunostimulation during childhood.

The immediate (type I) hypersensitivity consists of three stages:

1. *Sensitization:* in this phase the immune system identifies for the first time the foreign substance (allergen) and, consequently, the plasma cells synthesize IgE and IgG4 antibodies (against this allergen). These antibodies are to be bound to high affinity Fc receptors (FcεRI), present on the membrane of mast cells and basophils, and to low affinity Fc receptors (FcεRII) found on the surface of eosinophils, neutrophils, platelets and monocytes / macrophages. Allergen exposure occurs through injection, inoculation, inhalation, ingestion or direct contact.

2. *Immediate Response:* in this phase, subsequent to the sensitization period (usually of 15-30 days), the immune system identifies the allergen again, through one of the exposure routes, which binds to IgE on cell membranes, triggering the degranulation of mast cells and basophils with the release of preformed mediators contained in their granules (histamine, adenosine, chymase, tryptase, heparin) within 5 - 30 minutes from the exposure. The degranulation is the result of an increase in the intracellular calcium level. These preformed mediators are mainly responsible for the clinical manifestations which, in increasing order of severity, are: rhinitis, conjunctivitis, urticaria, bronchial asthma, laryngospastic angioedema and anaphylactic shock. Laryngospasm and anaphylactic shock are life-threatening medical emergencies that require immediate multi-level treatment (adrenergic agents, corticosteroids, antihistamines, beta-stimulants, intravenous fluid). Actually, anaphylactic shock is a well-known example of immediate type hypersensitivity reaction, inducing a diffuse organ hypoperfusion with failure of the peripheral circulation (distributive shock), possibly complicated by increased capillary permeability and fatal irreversible circulatory damage.

3. *Delayed Response:* after a few hours from allergen exposure, regardless of its persistence, secondary mediators (autacoids, cytokines), synthesized *de novo* by A2 phospholipase, are released from various inflammatory cells. These include MBP (Major Basic Protein) and ECP (Eosinophil Cationic Protein), which are the main causes of tissue damage.

ALLERGENS

The most known allergens inducing anaphylaxis are drugs (antibiotics, neuromuscular blockers, aspirin and NSAIDs), contrast media, sera and vaccines, natural rubber latex, insect venoms (hymenoptera, hemiptera), animal food (milk, eggs, shellfish), plant foods, such as fruits (avocado, banana, cantaloupe, cherry, chestnut, coffee, hazelnut, kiwi, mango, peanut, pineapple, strawberry) and vegetables (carrot, celery, chickpea, horseradish, ginseng, mushroom, rice, sesame, tomato, turnip, wheat, zucchini). In particular, anaphylactic reactions occur more frequently in patients with combined allergy to latex and plant foods for their glyco-epitopic commonality, giving rise to the so-called latex-fruit syndrome. Carbohydrate cross-reactive determinants (CCDs) are in fact carbohydrate moieties of glycoproteins that induce the production of highly cross-reactive IgE. They are oligosaccharide or polysaccharide derived from the assembly of monosaccharides such as mannose, fructose, fucose, galactose and are distinguished in N-glycans or O-glycans, according to their site of attachment to the protein. CCDs have been identified in different allergens of vegetal (latex, foods, pollens) or animal (venoms) origin. Recently, our risk management and research group (Roncati *et al.*) has reported the sentinel event of an intraoperative anaphylactic death from prolonged infusion of Thymoglobulin during orthotopic liver transplantation (OLT), resulting from recruitment of both mastocytes and basophils, activated and degranulated, in particular in the portal spaces and in the splenic sinuses (Figure 3). Post-mortem serological analysis on a preserved sample of the pre-OLT blood of the patient revealed specific IgE against CCDs, proving that anaphylactic reaction was triggered by mannitol excipient (Thymoglobulin carbohydrate excipient), rather than anti-thymocyte globulin itself. Mannitol (sorbitol isomer) is classified as a sugar alcohol, usually derived from fructose hydrogenation. Clinically, mannitol can been used as an osmotic laxative and diuretic agent in the treatment of intracranial hypertension, oliguric renal failure and acute glaucoma. The administration of mannitol should be avoided in multiallergic patients with specific IgE against CCDs. In these patients, the administration of hypertonic sodium solution is to be preferred, in order to prevent anaphylactic reactions (Roncati *et al.*).

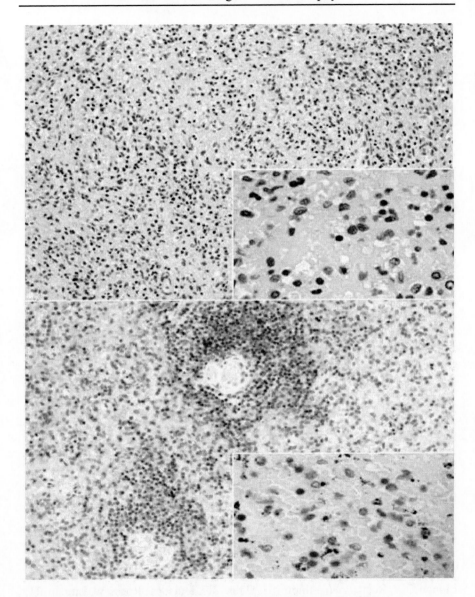

Figure 3. Unexpected intraoperative anaphylactic death due to mannitol (Thymoglobulin carbohydrate excipient). In the splenic red pulp degranulated mast cells (red stained by Pagoda red) and activated basophils (brown stained by immunohistochemical sequence DAB - 2D7) are noticeable.

CONCLUSION

It is well known that the spleen is supplied with a double circulation, that is an open circulation and a closed circulation. During the closed circulation the blood flow, arteriolar in origin, is periodically stopped in the splenic sinuses to allow the margining of aged erythrocytes and their subsequent destruction in the Billroth's cords. Our research group has found activated basophils, detected by 2D7 antibody, and degranulated mast cells, stained by Pagoda red, only in the sinuses of patients, who have died from anaphylactic shock. The special stainings have been performed on formalin-fixed paraffin-embedded splenic specimens coming from cases of anaphylactic death and from control-cases of non-anaphylactic death (Trani *et al.*). The periodic shutdown of the blood in the red pulp sinuses immobilizes mast cells and basophils, usually few in circulating blood, and facilitates the contact between their high affinity IgE-receptors and the allergens, representing the key moment of the allergic response. On the basis of our findings the spleen can be considered the human shock organ.

REFERENCES

Al-Lazikani B, Lesk AM, Chothia C. Standard conformations for the canonical structures of immunoglobulins. *J Mol Biol.* 1997; 273(4): 927–48.

Heyman B. Complement and Fc-receptors in regulation of the antibody response. *Immunol Lett.* 1996; 54(2–3): 195–9.

Karasuyama H, Tsujimura Y, Obata K, Mukai K. Role for basophils in systemic anaphylaxis. *Chem Immunol Allergy.* 2010; 95: 85-97.

Latasa M, Diéguez I, Sanz ML, Parra A, Pajarón MJ, Oehling A. Fruit sensitization in patients with allergy to latex. *J Investig Allergol Clin Immunol.* 1995; 5(2): 97-102.

Litman GW, Rast JP, Shamblott MJ, Haire RN, Hulst M, Roess W, Litman RT, Hinds-Frey KR, Zilch A, Amemiya CT. Phylogenetic diversification of immunoglobulin genes and the antibody repertoire. *Mol Biol Evol.* 1993; 10(1): 60–72.

Malandain H. IgE-reactive carbohydrate epitopes-classification, cross-reactivity, and clinical impact. *Eur Ann Allergy Clin Immunol.* 2005; 37(4): 122-8.

Mian I, Bradwell A, Olson A. Structure, function and properties of antibody binding sites. *J Mol Biol.* 1991; 217(1): 133–151.

Padlan EA. Anatomy of the antibody molecule. *Mol Immunol.* 1994; 31(3): 169-217.

Richet G. The discovery of anaphylaxis, a brief but triumphant encounter of two physiologists. *Hist Sci Med.* 2003; 37(4): 463-9.

Roncati L, Barbolini G, Scacchetti AT, Busani S, Maiorana A. Unexpected death: anaphylactic intraoperative death due to Thymoglobulin carbohydrate excipient. *Forensic Sci Int.* 2013; 228(1-3); 28-32.

Roncati L, Barbolini G, Cavallini G. The anaphylactic risk for mannitol in allergic patients. *Emerg Med J.* 2013.

Roux K. Immunoglobulin structure and function as revealed by electron microscopy. *Int Arch Allergy Immunol.* 1999; 120(2): 85–99.

Schwartz LB. Effector cells of anaphylaxis: mast cells and basophils. *Novartis Found Symp. 2004*; 257: 65-74.

Trani N, Bonetti LR, Gualandri G, Barbolini G. Immediate anaphylactic death following antibiotics injection: splenic eosinophilia easily revealed by pagoda red stain. *Forensic Sci Int.* 2008; 181(1-3): 21-5.

Voehringer D. Basophils in allergic immune responses. *Curr Opin Immunol.* 2011; 23(6): 789-93.

In: Globulins
Editor: Sheila D. Milford

ISBN: 978-1-63117-781-1
© 2014 Nova Science Publishers, Inc.

Chapter 3

BIOCHEMICAL CHARACTERISTICS, AND NUTRACEUTICAL AND TECHNOLOGICAL USES OF AMARANTH GLOBULINS

Oliviert Martínez-Cruz[1], Francisco Cabrera-Chávez[2] and Octavio Paredes-López[3]

[1]Departamento de Investigación y Posgrado en Alimentos, Universidad de Sonora, Sonora, México
[2]UnidadAcadémica de Ciencias de la Nutrición y Gastronomía, Universidad Autónoma de Sinaloa, Culiacán, Sinaloa, México
[3]Centro de Investigación y de EstudiosAvanzados del IPN, Irapuato, Guanajuato, México

ABSTRACT

Seed storage proteins have been nutritional and functionally valuable in the food industry and for human consumption. The Osborne's classical technique has been used to extract and classify seed storage proteins; additionally, in the last decades molecular properties have been also used for their characterization. Amaranth proteins, most of them being globulins (salt soluble proteins), have good essential amino acid levels. The nutritional, nutraceutical and technological properties shown by amaranth make it highly attractive to be incorporated into food formulations and to complement or replace some conventional cereal grains. The functional properties of its proteins provide good technological characteristics to food matrices. Several studies have shown that globulins are involved in some immunological processes suggesting that the immune-stimulating effects may lead to B lymphocyte activation and subsequent T cell proliferation *in vitro*. Other bioactive properties have been found in peptides from globulins mainly as outstanding antihypertensive agents. The previous characteristics, plus some others, are showing that the strong potential of amaranth and especially of its globulins should lead both of them to wider food and nutraceutical uses.

INTRODUCTION

The challenge to increase food and agricultural production in order to gain food security still persists after about 50 years of the Green Revolution (Hobbs, 2007). The first Millennium Development Goal is to reduce hunger and poverty by 2015 (Dixon et al., 2006). The demand for food is increasing, not only because of the growing population, but also because of the need to provide more nutritious food with high protein quality and nutraceutical compounds.

Water resources, especially surface and ground water will be more limited as domestic and industrial needs increase just as it is limited in semi-desert zones with low precipitation, and so future crops must be more suited to low water use. Amaranth is a crop naturally resistant to water deficit and it is a good source of nutritious seeds; the seeds have high amounts of protein containing essential amino acids, also their oil contains high levels of squalene, an important precursor for all steroids (He et al., 2002), among other important nutritious compounds such as dietary fiber and minerals like magnesium, phosphorus, copper, and specially manganese.

Amaranth is one of the few multi-purpose crops, which can supply grains and tasty leafy vegetables of high nutritional quality as a food and animal feed, and additionally it is an ornamental plantbecause of an attractive inflorescence coloration (Mlakar et al., 2009). Besides protein, the grains are a good source of dietary fibre and minerals, such as magnesium, phosphorus, copper, and especially manganese.

Amaranth flour is used as a thickener in gravies, soups, stews, and custards, and maybe blended with wheat flour in the preparation of unleavened flat bread known as "chapattis" in India, and "tortillas" in Latin America. The amaranth has great potential in the production of gluten free cereal based products, such as bread, pasta and confectionary products (Alvarez-Jubete et al., 2010).

Amaranth

Amaranthus species have different centers of domestication and origin being widely distributed in Central and North America and South American Andes. It is estimated that there are 87 species of Amaranthus, the majority of which are wild (Stallknecht and Schultz-Schaeffer, 1993). Some species are cosmopolitan, being both introduced and naturalized plants, with a weed-like behaviour, such as *Amaranthus retroflexus*, *Amaranthus hybridus*, *Amaranthus powellii*, and *Amaranthus viridis*. Amongst the cultivated species, *Amaranthus cruentus*, *Amaranthus hypochondriacus* and *Amaranthus caudatus* stand out and considered as pseudocereals, with high seed protein content and balanced amino acid composition (Srivastava and Roy, 2013). Some of them are used as food (grain), others as ornamental (flower) and some are simple weeds with no use at all. *Amaranthus caudatus*, *Amaranthus cruentus*, and *Amaranthus hipochondriacus* are the most widely used for grain (Teutonico and Knorr, 1985). Due to their great variety of the Amaranthus genus, taxonomic classification is very complex (Weber, 1990).

Amaranth, a dicotyledoneous plant, is an ancient crop with several agronomic advantages: fast growth, relatively high performance and tolerance to extreme conditions and pour soils. It seeds and leaves are edible, so it can be fully utilized (Paredes-López et al., 1998).

Amaranth (*Amaranthus hypochondriacus*) was greatly appreciated by the advanced Meso-American civilizations of the New World as a basic food in their diets. Due to the amaranth nutraceutical characteristics is also called by some authors "the food crop of the 21st century" (Lehmann, 1996: Chaturvedi et al., 1997; Guzmán-Maldonado and Paredes-López, 1998). However, its association with religious rites resulted in its cultivation being discouraged after the Spanish conquest (Guzmán-Maldonado and Paredes-López, 1998). This pseudo-cereal has been identified as a crop comparable with most potential food and feed resources, because of the exceptional nutritional-fuctional quality of its seed storage proteins (Guzmán-Maldonado and Paredes-López, 1998).

Aguilar et al. (2013) determined proteins, total lipids, dietary fiber, amino acid and fatty acids profile of two new varieties: *Amaranthus cruentus* var. Candil, and *Amarantus hypochondriacus* var. Dorado. A complete chemometric assessment was carried out to identify every new variety and advanced line between each other, using as variables the amino acid and fatty acid profiles. It is well known that there are two major classes of globulins on the basis of their sedimentation coefficients: 11S globulin (i.e. legumin) is a hexamer with MW 300 to 400 kDa and composed of six subunits, each subunit consisting of an acidic polypeptide (27-37 kDa) and a basic polypeptide (20-24 kDa) linked by disulfide bounds; and 7S globulin (i.evicilin) is generally a trimer with MW 150-200 kDa and consists of nonidentical subunits a (57-68 kDa), a' (57-72 kDa) and b (42-52 kDa) (Wright, 1987). The 11S proteins are distributed in the seeds of many mono- and di-cotyledonous plants, e.g., legumes, rice, oat, sesame, rape, quinoa, pumpkin, while 7S proteins are present in legumes (Fukushima, 1991; Shewry, 1995, 1998).

The 7S is a trimeric glycoprotein (170-141 kDa) composed of six different combinations of three subunits, α (57 kDa), α' (58 kDa), and β (42 kDa) associated via hydrophobic interactions (Utsumi and Kinsella, 1985). The 11S consists of two opposed hexagonal rings each containing three hydrophobically associated pair of disulfide-linked acidic (37-35 kDa) and basic (20-18 kDa) subunits.

In amaranth, these proteins are predominantly in the form of saline-soluble globulins which, based upon their structure similarities and sedimentation coefficients, have been classified as either 7S (vicilin-like) or 11S (legumin-like) proteins. The major globulin component, the 11S type, is removed from the flour in two subfractions of similar size; one of them is easily obtained with neutral saline solutions, whereas the other requires several treatments before being extracted and was named globulin I by Chen and Paredes-López (1997) or albumin-2 by Konishi et al. (1991) and Martínez et al. (1997). Konishi et al. (1991) compared the relative amount of the latter subfraction with albumin-1 and globulin and obtained the following relative proportions: albumin-1:globulin:albumin-2, 1:0.55:0.67. Although having a similar polypeptide composition, albumin-2 possesses higher denaturation enthalpy, lower solubility in neutral aqueous solutions, and higher tendency to polymerize than salt soluble globulin (Castellani et al., 1998).

On the other hand, cereal prolamins are normally deficient in lysine and tryptophan, such as in maize and rice, whereas legume globulins show deficiency in sulfur-containing amino acids, such as methionine and cysteine. Consequently, diets based on a single cereal or legume species result in amino acid deficiencies (Shewry, 1995; Rascón-Cruz et al., 2004).

Globulins are a major amaranth protein fraction, with the 11S globulin, called amarantin, representing 90 and 18.6% of the total globulins and total seed proteins, respectively (Romero-Zepeda and Paredes-López, 1996; Marcone, 1999). In addition, amarantin also possesses remarkable heat stability and emulsifying properties and is therefore expected to be useful as a potential emulsifier with high nutritional value (Konishi and Yoshimoto, 1989). However, it shows lower solubility in an acidic pH (4.5-6.8) due to the effect of its isoelectric point, which lies within this pH range (Konishi and Yoshimoto, 1989).

Amarantin is a homohexameric molecule with an apparent molecular weight ~300-400 kDa comprising subunits of 53 kDa, each of which consists of an acidic polypeptide (34-36 kDa) of 265 amino acids with a theoretical isoelectric point (pI) of 5.79 and a basic polypeptide (22-24 kDa) of 188 amino acids with a pI of 9.22, both linked by a disulfide bridge (Valdez-Ortiz et al., 2005). Moreover, although amarantin appears to have features similar to those of other 11S-type globulins, it has the advantage of containing a higher level of essential amino acids, which is closer to the optimum required amounts for humans established by international health organizations (FAO/WHO, 1991; Barba de la Rosa et al., 1996). There is considerable N-terminal protein sequence similarity reported among the polypetides of the seed globulins and that similarity extends over diverse plants which must be due to a constrained protein structure necessary to fulfill the basic physiological role of storage proteins as a source of nitrogen for the developing seedling and for a stable accumulation in the seed. (Barba de la Rosa et al., 1996)

Overexpression of Amaranth Proteins

With the modern advances in genomics, proteomics and bioinformatics, the number of proteins being produced using recombinant techniques is exponentially increasing. High throughput screening approaches are being performed to rapidly identify proteins with a potential application as therapeutic, diagnostic or industrial enzymes (Arnau et al., 2006).

A number of strategies are being considered to dress the problem of seed processing and nutritional quality. One approach is to modify the existing proteins of seeds in order to improve their balance of essential amino acids and functional properties simultaneously. Alternatively, it may be possible to transfer genes encoding proteins with high nutritional-functional value to crops of traditional agronomic importance (Sindhu et al., 1997; Shewry, 1998; Rooke et al., 1999). Currently, biotechnology and molecular biology offer an opportunity to effect improvements through rational modification-expression of genes or cDNAs coding for heterologous proteins with high nutritional-functional quality, using protein-engineering techniques (Shewry, 1998).

Previous studies on amarantin showed that its cDNA can be expressed in *Escherichia coli*, exhibiting electrophoretic, immunochemical, and suface hydrophobicity properties similar to those of native amarantin from amaranth seed (Segura-Nieto et al., 1994; Chen and Paredes-López, 1997; Osuna-Castro et al., 2000). One strategy is the introduction, through genetic engineering, of genes encoding proteins with high nutritional value into food crops with agronomic importance (Katsube et al., 1999; Stöger et al., 2001; Yang et al., 2002). Thus, it would be advantageous to express novel seed proteins such as amarantin in maize grains with the objective of improving amino acid composition. Moreover, the molecular and functional characterization of the expressed amarantin would facilitate understanding of the mechanisms of expression, processing, and deposition of amarantin in transgenic plants.

Amarantin is an excellent candidate to be overexpressed in transgenic plants of important crops, such as maize or rice, to improve their functional properties as protein ingredients or their grain's nutritional value. However, high-yield expression and single purification procedures for this important protein would aid in determining whether the recombinant non-modified or bioengineered protein is able to acquire the proper molecular conformation. Moreover, producing appreciable amounts of purified recombinant amarantin in transgenic plants allows for structural-functional studies (Rascón-Cruz et al., 2004).

Rascón-Cruz et al. (2004) transformed a tropical maize genotype using an amaranth 11S globulin cDNA encoding one of the most important storage proteins (amarantin) of the seed. Southern-blot analysis confirmed the integration of the amarantincDNA, and copy number ranged from one to more than ten copies per maize genome. Western-blot and ultracentrifugation analyses of transgenic maize indicated that the expressed recombinant amarantin precursors were processed into the mature form, and accumulated stably in maize endosperm. Total protein and some essential amino acids of the best expressed proteins were susceptible to digestion by simulated gastric and intestinal fluids, and it was tested that they showed no allergenic activity. These findings demonstrate the feasibility of using genetic engineering to improve the amino acid composition of grain crops.

For the production of recombinant proteins, various expression systems using prokaryotic cells, yeast cells, or mammalian cells have been established (Yokoyama, 2003). To achieve a high level expression of a target protein, *E. coli* is the most commonly employed host cell for an expression system because of its distinct and well-studied genetic background, abundant available plasmids, and its possibility for gene manipulation. Moreover, production of peptides using the *E. coli* expression systems is more environmental friendly and less expensive compared to chemical synthesis.

In 2000 Osuna-Castro et al. reported the overexpression, purification, and *in vitro* refolding or the 11S globulin from amaranth seed in *E. coli*. The expressed protein exhibited electrophoretic, immunochemical, and surface hydrophobicity properties similar to those of native amarantin from amaranth seed. Also, the recombinant protein was refolded *in vitro* using two different methods.

Amarantin expression in seeds of transgenic maize and tobacco resulted in important increses of seed protein content and quality (Rascón-Cruz et al., 2004; Valdez-Ortiz et al., 2005). Valdez-Ortiz et al. (2005) reported a one-step purification and structural characterization of a recombinant His-tag 11S globulin expressed in transgenic tobacco. The results showed that the His tag did no change the biochemical and physicochemical properties of amarantin. The strategy presented for rapid and high-yield expression and purification procedure should facilitate structure-function studies for this nutritional protein.

Mature amarantin extracted from seeds has a hexameric structure with a molecular mass of 398 kDa. SDS-PAGE analysis under reducing conditions resolved three different bands: one of 50-52 kDa, corresponding to proamarantin, and two more bands of 31-34 and 22-24 kDa corresponding to acidic and basic chains, respectively (Barba de la Rosa et al., 1996; Chen and Paredes-López, 1997). A His-tagged version was expressed and accumulated in *E. coli* as a trimer, and proamarantin was purified by immobilized metal affinity chromatography (Medina-Godoy et al., 2004). Expression in plants was also performed including tobacco and maize, resulting in a proper accumulation pattern and in important increases of seed protein content with no-allergic reaction in mice fed with transgenic plants (Rascón-Cruz et al., 2004; Sinagawa-García et al., 2004; Valdez-Ortiz et al., 2005). Moreover, the acidic subunit of amarantin is the candidate for protein modification. This fraction harbors four hypervariable regions of the five detected in the 11S seed globulins (Wright, 1988; Dickinson et al., 1990; Adachi et al., 2003). A His-tagged version of the acidic subunit was expressed in *E. coli* and was purified by immobilized metal affinity chromatography (Luna-Suárez et al., 2008).

Castro-Martínez et al. (2012) reported the overexpression of a modified protein from amaranth seed in *E. coli* and the effect of environmental conditions on the protein expression. The results indicated that the yield of modified protein could be increased by up 3-fold in biorreactor as compared with flask. In addition, the temperature, the agitation speed and the oxygen were significant factors on the expression of the protein.

Thus, amarantin protein has been expressed successfully in bacteria, yeast and plants (Medina-Godoy et al., 2004; Medina-Godoy et al., 2006; Valdez-Ortiz et al., 2007; Valdez-Ortiz et al., 2005). The utility of the acidic-subunit as an engineered model to evaluate proteins processing, enhanced nutritional and functional properties has been demonstrated (Luna-Suárez et al., 2008; Luna-Suárez et al., 2010).

Using protein engineering, further characteristics could be incorporated to this high-nutritional protein, such as biopeptides or modified amino acid sequence, to enhance functional and nutraceutical properties.

Uses of Amaranth Proteins in the Food Industry

Proteins are commonly employed as food ingredients on the basis of their importance in the human diet. Animal proteins are widely used in food formulation because of their high nutritional value and their versatile functional performance. However, the high cost of animal proteins makes vegetable proteins the main dietary component for most of the world's population, and as an alternative protein sources, more economic and with high nutritional quality and bioavailability. Several plant proteins have been studied to achieve this goal, including storage proteins from soy, pea and sunflower (Scilingo et al., 2002; González-Pérez and Vereijken, 2007).

To be used in food industry, the selected proteins should display a wide range of functional properties, which are closely related to their structure (Kinsella and Phillips, 1989). Several physical, chemical and enzymatic treatments have been used to modify the functional properties of seeds proteins. Thermal treatment is a physical procedure frequently used in food industry for modifying protein functionality (Boye et al., 1997). Depending on the thermal stability of proteins and the heating conditions, proteins may be either partially or completely denatured and sometimes may be aggregated changing their functional behavior (Petruccelli and Añón, 1995).

Usually, the enzymatic modification is preferable due to milder processing conditions, easier control of the reaction, and minimal formation of by-products (Mannheim and Cheryan, 1992). While protein hydrolysates with a high level of hydrolysis (>10%) are used as nutritional supplements, protein hydrolysates with a low degree of hydrolysis (1-10%) are usually produced to improve the functional performance relative to that of the original proteins, mainly foaming and emulsifying properties (Rodríguez Patino et al., 2007).

In this sense, Scilingo et al. (2002) reported the improvevent of the amaranth protein isolate solubility, and consequently, the isolate was modified by proteolytic treatments with two plant proteases (cucurbita and papain) and proteolysis was stopped either by freezing or by thermal treatment. The solubility and structural characteristics of all the modified isolates were analyzed in order to establish their structure-function relationship.

Additionally, Condés et al. (2009) prepared protein isolates from *Amaranthus hypocondriacus* hydrolyzed with trypsin. The structure, solubility and foaming properties were analyzed. Protein solubility increased markedly with hydrolysis, while changes in foaming properties were less dramatic. Nevertheless, foams obtained with amaranth protein hydrolysates were more dense and stable than those prepared with non-digested proteins, specially for foams produced with the protein hydrolysate concentration of 2.5 mg of solid matter per mL.

One of the most important functional properties of proteins is gelation. The phenomenon of heat-induced globular protein gelation was extensively described (Clark et al., 2001). Gelation capacity and gel properties are straightforward related to their rheological properties. Protein gels are composed by a protein matrix within which the aqueous phase is occluded. Rheological properties such as viscoelasticity and texture are closely related with microstructure of the matrix gel. The gels of fine-stranded matrix are harder and retain more water than those of more open matrices. The contributions of covalent and non-covalent bonds to gel texture and viscoelasticity are different in mature. Disulfide bonds usually play and important role in increasing gel matrix hardness whereas hydrogen and hydrophobic interactions are responsible for keeping network structure (Zheng et al., 1993).

The aim of Avanza et al. (2005) was to study the gelation kinetic of amaranth proteins and deepen the study of the influence of thermal treatment and protein concentration on viscoelastic and textural properties of amaranth protein gels. The types of gels analyzed were elastic in nature, of high hardness, fracturability and cohesiveness, although presented low adhesiveness. Depending on protein and thermal conditions, amaranth proteins were able to form self-supporting gels that could be applied in different gel-like foods.

Kaur et al. (2010) reported the plant, grain and flour characteristics of 48 *Amaranthus hypochondriacus* and 11 *Amaranthus caudatus* lines. The *A.*

caudatus lines had a higher protein content, fat content and tendency for retrogradation, and lower α-amylase activity as compared to *A. hypochondriacus* lines. The results reflected that the lines with higher α-amylase activity showed a lower peak viscosity, breakdown, final viscosity and gel hardness, and a higher pasting temperature.

Borneo and Aguirre (2008) evaluated the potential of the green material of the amaranth plant (leaves) as component for pasta production and its effect on the pasta quality and consumer acceptance. Amaranth pasta samples were evaluated for its chemical composition, cooking quality, textural, and sensory/consumer acceptance. Pasta made with dried amaranth leaves had similar properties as green pasta made with dried spinach leaves. This study pointed out that amaranth leaves could be technically used for pasta production and that consumer acceptance of this pasta is similar to commercial green one.

The amaranth flours have been also used to formulate pasta, cookies and breads. These food products are conventionally elaborated with wheat flour. The unique viscoelastic properties of wheat gluten proteins (water insoluble proteins) give the final characteristics in these foodstuffs.

From the perspective of functionality, the main challenge in non-wheat breads, cookies and pasta products is to mimic the viscoelastic properties of wheat dough. In this sense, native amaranth proteins are mainly monomeric polypeptides (Lorenz, 1981), however, they are able to form aggregates, stabilized by di-sulfide bonds, under certain conditions as the pre-gelatinization followed by extrusion processes (Cabrera-Chávez et al., 2012). Thus, the molecular re-arrangement implies textural modifications that can be modulated to mimic the final characteristics of wheat products like pasta.

In cereals flour dough, starches also contribute to its rheological behavior. In amaranth-based baking foods, the water-holding capacity is higher when the starches are damaged as in popped amaranth, but the modifications in globulins due to heating during the popping also contribute to this characteristic (Calderón de la Barca et al., 2010). Furthermore, the mixing profile of wheat dough is more similar to this kind of amaranth than to raw amaranth. Raw amaranth dough has higher proportion of elastic component than the viscous one (Houben et al., 2010). Therefore, when amaranth is popped, the elastic component increases even more respect to the viscous one (Markowski et al., 2006) causing the mentioned characteristics in the mixing properties.

Immuno-Nutritional and Other Physiological Functions of Amaranth Globulins and Peptides

Beyond the functional and nutritional characteristics of amaranth globulins, these proteins and some of their peptides have medical properties. For instance, the diet is considered a risk factor for several chronic diseases, including cancer and some authors have studied the effect of inclusion of amaranth grains components in diets on the transformation of normal cells into detectable tumors. According to Yu et al. (2001) an amaranth (*A. caudatus*) lectin can recognize and bind to a tumor factor. In their study they showed that the diets containing this lectin may act as a proliferation marker of malignant gastro-intestinal epithelial cells and that it may have a role in diagnosing intestinal cancer.

Respect to medical advantages, isolated proteins from amaranth (*A. mantegazzianus*) have shown antitumoral properties (antiproliferative effect) which were tested in several tumor cells lines (MC3T3E1, UMR106, Caco-2 and TC7). In agreement to Barrio and Añon (2010) these isolated polypeptides inhibit cell adhesion and induces apoptosis and necrosis in the malignant cell UMR106.

Amaranth proteins contain a peptide similar to an anticancer compound, called lunasin (Silva-Sánchez et al., 2008), found also in others grains as wheat, soy and barley (Jeonget al., 2002; Jeong et al., 2007 and González de Mejía et al., 2004). Lunasin has a relatively high content (~10%) of aspartic acid (Jeong et al., 2003) as amarantin (Barba de la Rosa et al., 1994). This characteristic suggests a relevant involvement of the acidic regions into a lunasin epitope.

Food allergy is a type I hypersensitivity reaction, responsible for a variety of symptoms and may be mediated or not by IgE antibodies. Thus, since the allergic response against amaranth macronutrients is rarely among food allergies, this pseudocereal has been widely used to formulate non-allergenic food products. In fact, Kasera et al. (2013) have barely published the first case of anaphylaxis caused by the consumption of this grain (*A. paniculatus*). Beyond the 'hypoallergenicity' of amaranth, it can inhibit the production of IgE and increase the cytokine Th1 synthesis, as a result of suppressing the cascade of allergenicity for specific antigens (Hibi et al., 2003).

According to Lin et al., (2005) *A. spinosus* proteinaceous water extracts and mainly a 313 kDa globulin have immuno-stimulating activity on primary splenocytes evaluated in a murine model, more specific on both B and T cells. However, bulk splenocytes stimulated by an adequate concentration of amaranth protein extracts exhibit higher proliferation rate than that of isolated B and T cells, suggesting interactions between these two cells. This could be due to T cells in bulk splenocyteswhich are activated throughout a secondary signaling from stimulated B cells, leading to the T cell proliferation. It has been found that B cells act as antigen presenting cells for CD4+ T cell priming if B cell and T cell coexist (Constant, 1999). Then the cytokines related to T helper cells may interact with B cells and regulate their differentiations (Gagro and Gordon, 1999). Thus, amaranth proteinaceous water extracts directly stimulate the proliferation of B lymphocytes and suggest the possibility of activated B cells, subsequently delivering a second signal to activate T cells. Moreover, these amaranth components stimulate both Th1 and Th2 cytokines production by splenocytes, however, the secretion of IL-5, IL-6 and IL-10 cytokines (Th2 profile) is higher than IL-2 and IFN-gamma cytokines (Th1 profile) (Lin et al., 2005). It is highlighted the reduced production of IL-4, that is involved into the B cell switching to IgE and consequently in the development of food allergies, when amaranth is consumed (Hibi et al., 2003). Thus, since the different immuno-modulatory principles might utilize diverse mechanisms (humoral and cellular immune responses), the protein-bioactive components in amaranth extracts may have potential for applications in immune-pharmacology. Therefore, it is necessary to characterize and identify the sequences in amaranth water soluble proteins involved in the immune-stimulatory processes.

Anti-Hypertensive Properties of Amaranth Proteins and Peptides

The modern diet together with a sedentary lifestyle has produced an epidemic of nutritionally related deceases. Hypertension, defined as an elevation of systolic and/or diastolic blood pressure above 140/90 mmHg, is one of these important diseases in our society, given its high prevalence and its role in cardiovascular diseases, including coronary heart disease, peripherialarterial disease, end-stage renal disease and stroke (Glasser, 2001; Chobanian et al., 2003; Seppo et al., 2003; Madureira et al., 2010). The control of hypertension through the diet has been a focal point for public health and mass media attention (Huffman et al., 2012, Sacks and Campos, 2010).

Angiotensin I converting enzyme (EC 3.4.15.1; ACE) is the key enzyme in rennin angiotensin systems. ACE increases blood pressure by both converting the inactive decapeptide angiotensin I to the potent vasoconstrictor angiotensin II, and inactivating the vasodilator bradykinin (Figure 1). Because ACE activity is closely associated with the development of hypertension and arteriosclerosis (Chobanian et al., 1990), *in vitro* inhibition of angiotensin II formation has been used for screening therapeutic agents such as ACE inhibitors against hypertension and arteriosclerosis.

Drugs that inhibit the renin-angiotensin system (important regulator of blood pressure), either by inhibiting ACE or by blocking angiotensin (AT1) receptors, are widely used in the treatment of hypertension. Chemically synthesized hypotensive drugs, such as captopril, propranolol, and losartan are still broadly used to treat and prevent hypertension. Nevertheless, these drugs are reported to have many side effects such as dry cough, taste disturbances, skin rashes, and many other dysfunctions of human organs (Fitzgerald and Meisel, 2000).

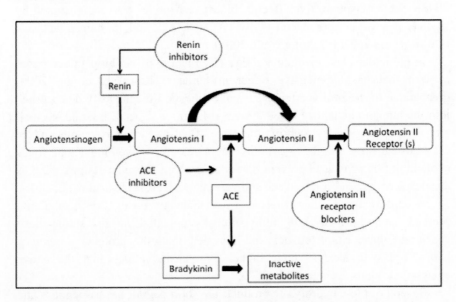

Figure 1. Renin-angiotensin system regulation and the involvement of peptides from amaranth. These sequences can act as inhibitors of angiotensin-converting enzyme (ACE) and even as blockers of angiotensin II in cells.

The influence of nutritive compounds on prevention and treatment of hypertension has attracted considerable attention over the last decade. In addition to nutritional function, many functional food products have health benefits (FOSHU or foods for specified health use) because they possess several compounds capable of modulating some biological functions such as control of blood pressure (Miguel et al., 2004; Kang et al., 2012).

Among these compounds are peptides derived from food proteins that exert antihypertensive activity (Erdmann et al., 2008). These protein-derived bioactive peptides are inactive within the sequences of the parent proteins but can be released by enzymatic proteolysis during gastrointestinal digestion. Once liberated in the body, bioactive peptides many act as regulatory compounds with hormone-like activity; they usually contain 2-20 amino acids residues per molecule, but in some cases may consist of more than 20. Because of their health-enhancing potential and safety profiles bioactive peptides may be used as components in functional foods or nutraceuticals (Erdmann et al., 2008).

Antihypertensive peptides can be introduced into food proteins and/or concentrated for the purpose of treatment of a disease or disorder, for example in those people with cardiac or renal insufficiency or diabetes (Seppo et al., 2003). The antihypertensive effect of bioactive peptides was demonstrated by studies *in vivo* in spontaneously hypertensive rats and in human subjects (Quirós et al., 2007; Bütikofer et al., 2008).

In particular, the dipeptide Val-Tyr (VT) is one of the biopeptides tested *in vivo* that has hypotensive effect in humans (Kawasaki et al., 2000) comparable to the antihypertensive usual medication it can easily be absorbed into the human circulatory blood system (Matsui et al., 2002). Besides, small Val-Tyr peptide exerts an antiproliferative effect on vascular smooth muscle cells, which suggests the possibility of developing novel medicinal foods containing this peptide to prevent diseases involving vascular lesions, such as arteriosclerosis, insulin-resistance and vascular restenosis (Matsui et al., 2005).

According to in silico analysis (Silva-Sánchez et al., 2008) amaranth proteins have sequences with antihypertensive potential. *In vitro* studies have confirmed these characteristics and revealed that, the proteins previously hydrolyzed with alcalase have higher hypotensive effect than the native amaranth proteins (Tiengo et al., 2009).

Several of these hydrolysate products are short peptides as tri-peptides and even di-peptides (Silva-Sánchez et al., 2008). However, the anti-hypertensive effect of amaranth protein hydrolysates should be tested in *in vivo* models, although the *in vitro* anti-hypertensive effect of amaranth peptides is commonly tested as their capability to inhibit the angiotensin-converting-enzyme activity (Actis-Goretta et al., 2006).

Later, Luna-Suárez et al. (2010) reported the modification of the amarantin acidic subunit, with the insertion of four Val-Tyr in tandem ACE inhibitory biopeptides and the expression of this protein in *E. coli*. Thus, they are trying to develop a novel food protein with antihypertensive activity for the diets of hypertensive persons.

Also, the developing of an engineered amarantin with a high *in vitro* angiotensin I-converting enzyme inhibitory (ACEi) activity has been done, by incorporating four dipeptides Val-Tyr in tandem, at the hypervariable region number III of the 11S globulins, and the tripeptide Ile-Pro-Pro at the carboxyl terminal region corresponding to the acidic-subunit of amarantin, an then named it AMC3 (Arano-Varela et al., 2012; Castro-Martínez et al., 2012).

In these sense, Medina-Godoy et al. (2013) evaluated the *in vivo* effect of AMC3 enzymatic hydrolysates (AEH) produced in *E. coli* in spontaneously hypertensive rats by once-oral administration experiments. AEH administration at maximal dose (100 mg/Kg) significantly reduces the mean arterial pressure similar to the group treated with captopril (an angiotensin-converting enzyme inhibitor used for the treatment of hypertension). The study showed that enzymatic hydrolysates of AMC3 containing angiotensin-converting enzyme inhibitory peptides (4xVY and IPP) sequences had significant antihypertensive action by oral administration in spontaneously hypertensive rats.

Large-scale production of antihypertensive peptides (AHPs) in viable vehicles, for production of functional foods as alternative hypertension therapies is still a challenge. To achieve this, different approaches have been used including the overexpression of recombinant AHP precursor proteins, and the generation and expression of engineered proteins contained tandem repeats of some AHPs (Rosales-Mendoza et al., 2013).

Recently, the use of plan cell suspensions (PCS) has received considerable attention for the production of recombinant proteins, due to their benefits in comparison to systems that use animal or microbial cell cultures, and whole plants (Girard et al., 2004).

The use of PCS provides a number of advantages such as acceptable yields, low cost, consistency in product quality, ability to express proteins with post translational modifications, and low risk of contamination by mammalian viruses, blood-born pathogens and oncogens; futhermore, their relatively homogeneous cell population allows a rapid and uniform access to nutrients, precursors, growth hormones regulators and signal compounds for the cells, which gives a greater simplicity in the correct folding and assembling of multimeric protein, besides; the procedure of protein isolation and purification are considered fast and simple (Mustafa et al., 2011).

A modified version of amarantin carrying four antihypertensive biopeptides Val-Tyr into the acidic-subunit of the protein was expressed in cell suspension cultures of *Nicotiana tabacum* L. NT1. The presence of the transgene was confirmed using histological glucoronidase assay and PCR analysis and the accumulation and expression of the recombinant protein was detected using Western blot analysis. The results showed that the protein hydrolysate of transgenic calli had high levels of inhibition of the angiotesin converting enzyme, with an IC50 value of 3.5 µg mL-1. This was 10-fold lower than that of protein extracts of wild-type cells, with an IC50 of 29.0 µg mL-1 (Santos-Ballardo et al., 2013).

Trends in Medical Applications of Amaranth Globulins and Their Derivates

Bioactive peptides are important components of functional foods, since it is generally acknowledged that specific sequences within the parent food proteins can provide physiological benefits once they are released either by *in vivo* digestion, microbial fermentation, or *in vitro* enzymatic hydrolysis (Hartmann and Meisel, 2007).

In the past years, it has been shown that food proteins constitute a source of natural blood-lowering peptides with *in vivo* activity, milk proteins being the most thoroughly studied (Murray and FitzGerald, 2007). An increase in protein consumption seems to decrease arterial pressure in hypertensive patients.

In addition, some studies in hypertensive patients have demonstrated the antihypertensive effect of inhibitory peptides from diverse sources or from functional foods that contain such bioactive compounds. These studies have prompted the marketing of several formulations of nutraceutic foods, particularly fermented milks that can moderate hypertension and reduce cardiovascular risk, among other effects (Sibbel, 2007).

Fritz et al. (2011) reported the hydrolytic release of encrypted peptides with antihypertensive activity from storage proteins of *Amaranthus mantegazzianus*, determined by *in vitro* assays, and tested for the first time in animal model and by *ex vivo* assays. Intragastric administration of hydrolysates with hydrolysis degree of 45% was effective in lowering blood pressure of male spontaneously hypertensive rats (SHR). Experiments performed in papillary muscles isolated from hearts and with isolated aortic smooth muscle of SHR suggested that the hypotensive effect could be attributed to a lowering of the peripheral resistance. Finally, they reported that the amaranth hydrolysates would be acting at the level of the local or autocrine renin-angiotensin system.

On the other hand, diverse metabolic pathways produce radical species, while free radicals are used in various specific physiological functions. Free radicals in biological systems include reactive oxygen species (ROS) and reactive nitrogen species (NOS). Besides, the human body has diverse defense antioxidant mechanisms that can act at different levels of the oxidation process. The most important defense mechanisms are antioxidant enzymes, free radical scavengers, and metal chelators (Noguchi et al., 2000). When free radicals are generated in excess or when cellular defenses are deficient, biomolecules are damaged by a process named oxidative stress (Mendis et al., 2007). This process seems to be implicated in cellular aging and also in associated diseases such as atherosis, cardiovascular disease, cancer, neurological degenerative diseases, and others (Wei and Lee, 2002).

Due to the negative consequences of the oxidative processes, their inhibition both inside the organism and in food is important, this being an area of very intense research. Due to the current tendency to consume natural products and because of the demonstrated carcinogenic activity of the common synthetic antioxidants, there is a high demand of antioxidants of natural origin (Lindberg Madsen and Bertelsen, 1995). Vegetables contain numerous antioxidant compounds such as polyphenols, phytosterols, carotenoids, vitamins C and E, among others. While some proteins and protein hydrolysates have been also shown to posses antioxidant activity, this type of antioxidant compounds has been mucho less analysed. Antioxidant activity has been demonstrated in peptides derived from soy proteins (Chen et al., 1996), caseins (Hernández-Ledesma et al., 2005), soy and milk whey (Peña-Ramos and Xiong, 2003), just to mention some examples.

The presence in amaranth seeds of some phytochemicals e.g., lecitines, polyphenols, saponins, trypsin inhibitors, phylates with physiological effects on humans has been described [Guzman-Maldonado and Paredes-López, 1998, (Chapter 9)]. Regarding the antioxidant properties of amaranth, such activity has been attributed to polyphenolic and squalene present in the plant (Nsimba et al., 2008). Tironi and Añón (2010) analyzed the antioxidant activity of proteins or peptides from amaranth; they analyzed the presence of proteins and/or peptides with antioxidant activity in seeds from *Amaranthus manteggazianus*, and the potential improvement of the antioxidant activity by means of protein hydrolysis.

In this research they reported that the active molecules were distributed into the different protein fractions (albumin, globulin, and glutenin), the glutenin fraction being the one with the highest activity. In addition, alcalase hydrolysis was able to improve the scavenging activity of both the isolated and the protein fractions by producing the release of small peptides and/or free amino acids with such activity.

Later, Orsini Delgado et al. (2011) reported the simulation of the gastrointestinal digestion process performed in two different amaranth products: a protein isolate and an extensive alcalase-hydrolysate. They analyzed the antioxidant activity of the different preparations in order to evaluate the potential formation of active peptides due to the gastrointestinal digestion. Both the protein isolate and the alcalase-hydrolysate showed a potential capacity to scavenge free radicals, appearing as promising ingredients to formulate functional foods with antioxidant activity.

Additionally, the presence of a range of phytochemical compounds that contribute to nutraceutical properties of the seeds was determined as well by Barba de la Rosa et al. (2009). Due that polyphenols as rutin and nicotiflorinare in relatively high concentrations, amaranth seeds could be a source of phenolic compounds of high antioxidant properties.

Several studies suggested that amaranth's oil fraction could be responsible for its beneficial hypocholesterolaemic effects, due the favorable fatty acid profile and high content of some unsaponifiable components. In an experiment with rats, Grajeta (1997) observed a reduction of 37% and 33% of total cholesterol when the animals were fed with whole amaranth and defatted amaranth, respectively.

It was evaluated the cholesterol-lowering effect of extruded amaranth and amaranth oil in hypercholesterolemic rabbits(Plate and Arêas, 2002). The results demonstrated that the consumption of extruded amaranth reduces LDL and total cholesterol levels and may be another option to prevent coronary heart diseases. However, recent reports show that amaranth free of the lipid moiety is more efficient to produce reduction of blood cholesterol levels and concluded that other components, possibly the protein fraction, are responsible for these benefits (Berger et al., 2003).

A number of different mechanisms may explain the favorable effects of grains on cholesterolemia. A reduction in the intestinal absorption of cholesterol and/or bile acids, an increase in plasma cholesterol clearance through enhanced hepatic LDL-receptor activity, and changes in the hepatic biotransformation of cholesterol can all be implicated.

Mendonça et al. (2009) reported the digestibility of protein as well as the excretion of cholesterol and bile acid as the possible mechanisms for the hypocholesterolaemic effect. Cholesterol excretion was related to the hypocholesterolaemia but could not explain all the observed reduction. Their findings suggested that amaranth protein has a metabolic effect on endogenous cholesterol metabolism.

Furthermore, amaranth is appropriate for people who are allergic to gluten (Svirskis, 2003) and the seeds have about 7% of fat, which around of 8% is squalene, a highly regarded compound by the pharmaceutical industry. Amaranth oil and squalene are used for oncological treatments, sclerosis, malfunction of the brain, immunodeficient states, skin, stomach and liver diseases, wounds, bedsores, and ulcers (Bogolyubov, 1999).

ACKNOWLEDGMENTS

We acknowledge partial financial support for these studies by ConsejoNacional de Ciencia y Tecnología (Conacyt).

REFERENCES

Actis-Goretta, L., Ottaviani, J. L. & Fraga, C. G. (2006). Inhibition of angiotensin converting enzyme activity by flavonol-rich foods. *J. Agric. Food Chem.*, *54*, 229–34.

Adachi, M., Kanamori, J., Masuda, T., Yagasaki, K., Nikamura, K., Mikami, B. & Utsumi, S. (2003). Crystal structure of soybean 11S globulin: glycinin A3B4 homohexamer. *Proc. Natl. Acad. Sci. U. S. A.*, *100*, 7395–7400.

Aguilar, E. G., Peiretti, E. G., Uñates, M. A., Marchevsky, E. J., Escudero, N. L. & Camiña, J. M. (2013). Amaranth seed varieties.A chemometric approach. *Food Measure*, *7*, 199-206.

Akama, K., Kanetou, J., Shimosaki, S., Kawakami, K., Tsuchikura, S. & Takaiwa, F., (2009). Seed-specific expression of truncated OsGAD2 produces GABA-enriched rice grains that influence a decrease in blood pressure in spontaneously hypertense rats. *Transgenic Res., 18*, 865–876.

Alvarez-Jubete, L., Arendt, E. K. & Gallagher, E. (2010). Nutritive value of pseudocereals and their increasing use as functional gluten free ingredients. *Trends Food Sci. Technol.*, *21*, 106–113.

Arano-Varela, H., Domínguez-Domínguez, J. & Paredes-López, O. (2012). Effect of environmental conditions on the expression levels of a recombinant 11S amaranth globulin in *Escherichia coli. Recent Pat. Biotechnol.*, *6*, 23–31.

Arnau, J., Lauritzen, C., Petersen, G. E. & Pedersen, J. (2006). Current strategies for the affinity tags and tag removal for the purification of recombinant proteins. *Protein Expres. Purif.*, *48*, 1-13.

Avanza, M. V., Puppo, M. C. & Añón, M. C. (2005). Rheological characterization of amaranth protein gels. *Food Hydrocolloids*, *19*, 889-898.

Barba de la Rosa, A. P., Fomsgaard, I. S., Laursen, B., Mortensen, A. G., Olvera-Martínez, L., Silva-Sánchez, C., Herrera-Mendoza, A., González-Castañeda, J. & De León-Rodríguez, A. (2009). Amaranth (*Amaranthus hypochondriacus*) as an alternative crop for sustainable food production: Phenolic acids and flavonoids with potential impact on its nutraceutical quality. *J. Cereal Sci.*, *49*, 117-121.

Barba de la Rosa, A. P., Herrera-Estrella, A., Utsumi, S. & Paredes-López, O. (1996). Molecular characterization, cloning and structural analysis of a cDNA encoding an amaranth globulin. *J. Plant Physiol.*, *149*, 527-532.

Barba de la Rosa, A. P., Gueguen, J., Paredes-López, O. &Viroben, G. (1994). Fractionation procedures, electrophoretic characterization and amino acid composition of amaranth seed proteins. *J. Agric. Food Chem.*, *40*, 931–936.

Barrio, D. A. & Añón, M. C. (2010). Potential antitumor properties of a protein isolate obtained from the seeds of *Amaranthus mantegazzianus*. *Eur. J. Nutr.*, *49*,73–82.

Baytok, E., Aksu, T., Karsli, M.A. & Muruz, H. (2005). The effects of formic acid, molasses and inoculant as silage additives on corn silage composition and ruminal fermentation characteristics in sheep. *Turk. J. Vet. Anim. Sci.*, *29*, 469–474.

Berger, A., Monnard, I., Dionisi, F., Gumy, D., Lambelet, P. & Hayes, K. C. (2003). Preparation of amaranth flakes, crude oils, and refined oils for evaluation of cholesterol-lowering properties in hamster. *Food Chem.*, *81*, 119–124.

Bogolyubov, I. S. (1999). Reference book "Source of Health". Tverj, p. 62 (2nd ed.) [cited by Svirskis, A. (2003). Investigation of amaranth cultivation and utilization in Lithuania. *Agron. Res.*, *1*, 253–264.

Borneo, R. & Aguirre, A. (2008). Chemical composition, cooking quality, and consumer acceptance of pasta made with dried amaranth leaves flour. *LWT-Food Sci. Technol.*, *41*, 1748-1751.

Boye, J. I., Ma, C.-Y. & Halwarkar, V. R. (1997). Thermal denaturation and coagulation of proteins. In S. Damodaran, & A. Paraf (Eds.), Food proteins and their applications (pp. 25–55). New York: Marcel-Dekker.

Bütikofer, U., Meyer, J., Walther, B. & Wechsler, D. (2008). Ocurrence of the angiotensin-converting enzyme-inhibiting tripeptides Val-Pro-Pro and Ile-Pro- Pro in different cheese varieties of Swiss origin. *J. Dairy Sci., 91*, 29–38.

Calderón de la BarcaAM, Rojas-Martínez ME, Islas-Rubio AR & Cabrera-Chávez F (2010) Gluten-free breads and cookies of raw and popped amaranth flours with attractive technological and nutritional qualities. *Plant Foods Hum. Nutr.*, *65*, 241–246.

Castellani, O. F., Martínez, E. N. & Añón, C. M. (1998). Structural modifications of an amaranth globulin induced by pH and NaCl. *J. Agric. Food Chem.*, *46*, 4846-4853.

Castro-Martínez, C., Luna-Suárez, S. & Paredes-López, O. (2012). Overexpression of a modified protein from amaranth seed in *Escherichia coli* and effect of environmental conditions on the protein expression. *J. Biotechnol.*, *158*, 59–67.

Chatuverdi, A., Sarojini, G. & Devi, N. L. (1993). Hypocholesterolemic effect of amaranth seeds (*Amaranthus exculantus*). *Plant Foods Hum. Nutr., 44*, 63-70.

Chen, H., Muramoto, K., Yamauchi, F. & Nokihara, K. (1996). Antioxidant activity of designed peptides based on the antioxidative peptide derived from digests of a soybean peptide. *J. Agric. Food Chem.*, *44*, 2619–2623.

Chen, S. & Paredes-López, O. (1997). Isolation and characterization of the 11S globulin from amaranth seeds. *J. Food Biochem.*, *21*, 53-65.

Chobanian, A. V., Bakris, G. L., Black, H. R., Cushman, W. C., Green, L. A., Izzo, J. L., Jr., Jones, D. W., Materson, B. J., Oparil, S., Wright, J. T., Jr. & Roccella, E. J. (2003). National Heart, Lung, and Blood Institute Joint National Committee on Prevention, Detection, Evaluation, and Treatment of High Blood Pressure; National High Blood Pressure Education Program Coordinating Committee. The Seventh Report of the Joint National Committee on Prevention, Detection, Evaluation, and Treatment of High Blood Pressure: The JNC 7 report. *J. Am. Med. Assn.*, *289*, 2560–2572.

Chobanian, A. V., Haudenschild, C. C., Nickerson, C. & Drago, R. (1990). Antiatherogenic effect of captopril in the Watanabe heritable hyperlipidemic rabbit. *Hypertension*, *15*, 327–331.

Clark, A. H., Kavanagh, G. M. & Ross-Murphy, S. B. (2001). Globular protien gelation-theory and experiment. *Food Hydrocolloids*, *15*, 383–400.

Condés, M. C., Scilingo, A. A. & Añón, M. C. (2009). Characterization of amaranth proteins modified by trypsin proteolysis. Structural and functional changes. *LWT-Food Sci. Technol.*, *42*, 963-970.

Constant S. L. (1999). B lymphocytes as antigen-presenting cells for CD4+ T cell priming *in vivo*. *J. Immunol.*, *162*, 5695– 703.

Dickinson, C. D., Scott, M. P., Hussein, E. H., Argos, P. & Nielsen, N. C. (1990). Effect of structural modifications on the assembly of a glycinin subunit. *Plant Cell*, *2*, 403–413.

Dixon, J., Nalley, L., Kosina, P., La Rovere, R., Hellin, J. & Aquino, P. (2006). Adoption and economic impact of improved wheat varieties in the developing world. *J. Agric. Sci.*, *144*, 489–502.

Erdmann, K., Wheung, B. W. Y. &Schröder, H. (2008). The possible roles of food- derived bioactive peptides in reducing the risk of cardiovascular disease. *J. Nutr. Biochem.*, *19*, 643–654.

FAO/WHO (1991). Food and Agriculture Organization of the United Nations. In: FAO food and nutrition paper. Rome.

Fitzgerald, R. J. & Meisel, H. (2000). Milk protein-derived peptide inhibitors of angiotensin-I-converting enzyme. *Br. J. Nutr.*, *84*, S33–S37.

Cabrera-Chávez, F., Calderón de la Barca, A. M., Islas-Rubio, A. R., Marti, A., Marengo, M., Pagani, M. A., Bonomi, F. & Iametti, S. (2012). Molecular rearrangements in extrusion processes for the production of amaranth-enriched, gluten-free rice pasta. *LWT - Food Sci. Technol.*, *47*, 421-426.

Fritz, M., Vecchi, B., Rinaldi, G. & Añón, M. C. (2011). Amaranth seed protein hydrolysates have *in vivo* and *in vitro* antihypertensive activity. *Food Chem.*, *126*, 878-884.

Fukushima, D. (1991). Structures of plant storage proteins and their functions. *Food Rev. Internat.,7*, 353-381.

Gagro A. & Gordon, J. (1999). The interplay between T helper subset cytokines and IL-12 in directing human B lymphocyte differentiation. *Eur. J. Immunol.*, *29*, 3369– 3379.

Girard, L. S., Bastin, M. & Courtois D. (2004). Expression of the human milk protein sCD14 in tobacco plant cell culture. *Plant Cell Tiss. Org. Cult.*, *78*, 253–260.

Glasser, S. P. (2001). Hypertension syndrome and cardiovascular events. *Postgrad. Med.*, *110*, 29–36.

Gonzalez de Mejia, E., Vasconez, M., De Lumen, B. O. & Nelson, R. (2007). Lunasin concentration in different soybean genotypes, commercial protein, and isoflavoneproducts. *J. Agric. Food Chem.*, *52*, 5882–5887.

González-Pérez, S. &Vereijken, J. M. (2007). Sunflower proteins: overview of their physicochemical, structural and functional properties. *J. Sci. Food Agric.*, *87*, 2173–2191.

Grajeta, H. (1997). Effects of amaranthus (*Amaranthus cruentus*) seeds on lipid metabolism in rats. *Bromatologiai Chemia Toksykologiczna*, *30*, 25–30.

Guzmán-Maldonado, S. H. & Paredes-López, O. (1998). Biochemical and Processing Aspects. In: Mazza G (Ed) Functional foods. Technomic Publishing, Lancaster, Penn., pp 293–328.

Hartmann, R. & Meisel, H. (2007). Food-derived peptides with biological activity: from research to food applications. *Curr. Opin. Biotechnol.*, *18*, 163–169.

He, H. P., Cai, Y., Sun, M. & Corke, H. (2002). Extraction and purification of squelene from *amaranthus* grain. *J. Agric. Food Chem.*, *50*, 368–372.

Hernández-Ledesma, B., Dávalos, A., Bartolomé, B. & Amigo, L. (2005). Preparation of antioxidant enzymatic hydrolysates from α-lactoalbumin y β-lactoglobulin. Identification of active peptides by HPLC-MS/MS. *J. Agric. Food Chem.*, *52*, 588–593.

Hibi M, Hachimura S, Hashizume S, Obata T. &Kaminogawa S. (2003). Amaranth grain inhibits antigen-specific IgE production through augmentation of the IFN-gamma response *in vivo* and *in vitro*. *Cytotechnology*, *43*, 33-40.

Hobbs, P. R. (2007). Conservation agriculture: what is it and why is it important for future sustainable food production. *J. Agric. Sci.*, *145*, 127–137.

Houben, A., Götz, H., Mitzscherling, M. & Becker, T. (2010) Modification of the rheological behavior of amaranth (*Amaranthus hypocondriacus*) dough. *J. Cereal Sci.*, *51*, 350–356.

Huffman, M. D., Capewell, S., Ning, H., Shay, C. M., Ford, E. S. & Lloyd-Jones, D. M. (2012). Cardiovascular health behavior and health factor changes (1988–2008) and projections to 2020: Results from the National Health and Nutrition Examination Surveys. *Circulation*, *125*, 2595–2602.

Jeong, H. J., Jeong, J. B., Kim, D. S. & De Lumen, B. (2007), Inhibition of core histone acetylating by the cancer preventive peptide lunasin. *J. Agric. Food Chem.*, *55*, 632–637.

Jeong, H. J., Lam, Y. & De Lumen, B. O. (2002). Barley lunasin suppresses ras-induced colony formation and inhibits core histone acetylation in mammalian cells. *J. Agric. Food Chem.*, *50*, 5903–5908.

Jeong, H. J., Park, J. H., Lam, Y. & De Lumen, B. O. (2003). Characterization of lunasin isolated from soybean. *J. Agric. Food Chem.*, *51*, 7901–7906.

Kang, M. G., Kim, J. H., Ahn, B. H. & Lee, J. S. (2012). Characterization of new antihypertensive angiotensin I- converting enzyme inhibitory peptides from Korean traditional rice wine. *J. Microbiol. Biotechnol.*,*22*, 339–342.

Kasera, R., Niphadkar, P. V., Saran, A., Mathur, C. & Singh, A.B. (2013). First case report of anaphylaxis caused by Rajgira seed flour (*Amaranthus paniculatus*) from India: a clinico-immunologic evaluation. *Asian Pac. J. Allergy Immunol., 31*, 79-83.

Katsube, T., Kurisaka, N., Ogawa, M., Maruyama, N., Ohtsuka, R., Utsumi, S. &Takaiwa, F. (1999). Accumulation of soybean glycinin and its assembly with the glutelins in rice. *Plant Physiol.*, *120*, 1063–1073.

Kaur, S., Singh, N. &Rana, J. C. (2010). *Amaranthushypochondriacus* and *Amaranthuscaudatus*germplasm: Characteristics of plants, grain and flours. *Food Chem.*, *123*, 1227-1234.

Kawasaki, T., Seki, E., Osajima, K., Yoshida, M., Asada, K., Matsui, T. & Osajima, Y. (2000). Antihypertensive effect of valyl-tyrosine, a short chain peptide derived from sardine muscle hydrolyzate, on mild hypertensive subjects. *J. Hum. Hypertens.*, *14*, 519–523.

Kinsella, J. E. & Phillips, L. (1989). Structure-function correlationships in food proteins, film and foaming behavior. In J. E. Kinsella, & W. Soucie (Eds.), Food proteins (pp. 57–77). Champaign: The American Oil Chemistry Society.

Konishi, Y. & Yoshimoto, H. (1989). Amaranth globulins as a heat- stable emulsifying agent. *Agric. Biol. Chem.*, *53*, 3327- 3328.

Konishi, Y., Horikawa, K., Oku, Y., Azumaya, J. & Nakatani, N. (1991). Extraction of two albumin fractions from amaranth grains: comparison of some physicochemical properties and the putative localization in the grains. *Agric. Biol. Chem.*, *55*, 1745-1750.

Lehmann, J. W. (1996). Case history of grain amaranth as an alternative crop. *Cereal Foods World*, *41*, 399-411.

Lin, B. F., Chiang, B. L. & Lin, J. Y. (2005). *Amaranthus spinosus* water extract directly stimulates proliferation ofB lymphocytes *in vitro*. *Int. Immunopharmacol.*, *5*, 711-22.

Lindberg Madsen, H. & Bertelsen, G. (1995). Spices as antioxidants. *Trends Food Sci. Technol.*, *6*, 271–278.

Lorenz, K. (1981). *Amarantus hypochondriacus*- Characteristics of the starch and baking potential of the flour. *Starch/Stärke*, *33*, 149-153.

Luna-Suárez, S., Medina-Godoy, S., Cruz-Hernández, A. & Paredes-López, O. (2008). Expression and characterization of the acidic subunit from 11S Amaranth seed protein. *Biotechnol. J.*, *3*, 209–219.

Luna-Suárez, S., Medina-Godoy, S., Cruz-Hernández, A. & Paredes-López, O. (2010). Modification of the amaranth 11S globulin storage protein to produce an inhibitory peptide of the angiotensin I converting enzyme, and its expression in *Escherichia coli. J. Biotechnol.*, *148*, 240–247.

Madureira, A. R., Tavares, T., Gomes, A. M. P., Pintado, M. E. & Malcata, F. X. (2010). Physiological properties of bioactive peptides obtained from whey proteins. *J. Dairy Sci. ,93*, 437–455.

Mandal, S. &Mandal, R. K., (2000) Seed storage proteins and approaches for improvement of their nutritional quality by genetic engineering. *Current. Sci.*, *79*, 576–589.

Mannheim, A. & Cheryan, M. (1992). Enzyme-modified proteins from corn gluten meal: preparation and functional properties. *J. Am. Oil Chem. Soc.*, *69*, 1163–1169.

Marcone, M. F. (1999). Evidence confirming the existence of a 7S globulin-like storage protein in *Amaranthus hypochondriacus* seed. *Food Chem.*, *65*, 533-542.

Markowski, M., Ratajski, A., Konopko, H., Zapotoczny, P. & Majewska, K. (2006). Rheological behavior of hot-air-puffed amaranth seeds. *Int. J. Food Properties*, *9*, 195–203.

Martínez, E. N., Castellani, O. F. & Añón, M. C. (1997). Common molecular features among amaranth storage proteins. *J. Agric. Food Chem.*, *45*, 3832-3839.

Matsui, T., Tamaya, K., Sekji, E., Osajima, K., Matsumoto, K. & Kawasaki, T. (2002). Val- Tyr as a natural antihypertensive dipeptide can be absorbed into the human circulatory blood system. *Clin. Exp. Pharmacol. Physiol.*, *29*, 204–208.

Matsui, T., Ueno, T., Tanaka, M., Oka, H., Miyamoto, T., Osajima, K. & Matsumoto, K. (2005). Antiproliferative action of an angiotensin I-converting enzyme inhibitory peptide, Val-Tyr, via an L-type Ca^{2+} channel inhibition in cultured vascular smooth muscle cells. *Hypertens. Res.*, *28*, 545–552.

Medina-Godoy, S., Nielsen, N. C. & Paredes-López, O. (2004). Expression and characterization of a His-tagged 11S seed globulin from *Amaranthus hypochondriacus* in *Escherichia coli*. *Biotechnol. Progr.*, *20*, 1749–1756.

Medina-Godoy, S., Rodríguez-Yáñez, S. K., Bobadilla, N. A., Pérez-Villalva, R., Valdez-Ortiz, R., Hong, E., Luna-Suárez, S., Paredes-López, O. & Valdez-Ortiz, A. (2013). Antihypertensive activity of AMC3, an engineered 11S amaranth globulin expressed in *Escherichia coli*, in spontaneously hypertensive rats. *J. Funct. Foods*, *5*, 1441-1449.

Medina-Godoy, S., Valdez-Ortiz, A., Valverde, M. E. & Paredes- López, O. (2006). Endoplasmic reticulum-retention C-terminal sequence enhances production of an 11S seed globulin from *Amaranthus hypochondriacus* in *Pichia pastoris*. *Biotechnol. J.*, *1*, 1085–1092.

Mendis, E., Kim, M., Rajapakse, N. & Kim, S. (2007). An *in vitro* cellular analysis of the radical scavenging efficacy of chitooligosaccharides. *Life Sci.*, *80*, 2118–2127.

Mendonça, S., Saldiva, P. H., Cruz, R. J. & Arêas, J. A. G. (2009). Amaranth protein presents cholesterol-lowering effect. *Food Chem.*, *116*, 738-742.

Miguel, M., Recio, I., Gómez-Ruiz, J. A., Ramos, M.& López- Fandiño, R. (2004). Angiotensin I-converting enzyme inhibitory activity of peptides derived from egg white proteins by enzymatic hydrolysis. *J. Food Protect.*, *67*, 1914–1920.

Mlakar, S. G., Turinek, M., Jakop, M., Bavec, M. & Bavec, F. (2009). Nutrition value and use of grain amaranth: Potential future application in bread making. *Agricultura, 6*, 43–53.

Murray, B. A.& FitzGerald, R. J. (2007). Angiotensin converting enzyme inhibitory peptides derived from food proteins: Biochemistry, bioactivity and production. *Curr. Pharma. Des.*, *13*, 773–791.

Mustafa, N. R., De Winter, W., Van Iren, F. & Verpoorte, R. (2011). Initiation, growth and cryopreservation of plant cell suspension cultures. *Nat. Protoc.*, *6*, 715–742.

Nakahara, T., Sano, A., Yamaguchi, H., Sugimoto, K., Chikata, H., Kinoshita, E. & Uchida, R. (2010). Antihipertensive effect of peptide-enriched soy sauce-like seasoning and identification of its angiotensin I-converting enzyme inhibitory substances. *J. Agric. Food Chem.,58*, 821–827.

Noguchi, N., Watanabe, A. & Shi, H. (2000). Diverse functions of antioxidants. *Free Radical Res.*, *33*, 809–817.

Nsimba, R., Kikuzaki, H. & Konishi, Y. (2008). Antioxidant activity of various extracts and fractions of *Chenopodium quinoa* and *Amaranthus* spp. *Seeds Food Chem.*, *106*, 760–766.

Orsini Delgado, M. C., Tironi, V. A. & Añón, M. C. (2011). Antioxidant activity of amaranth protein or their hydrolysates under simulated gastrointestinal digestion. *LWT-Food Sci. Technol.*, *44*, 1752-1760.

Osuna-Castro, J. A., Rascón-Cruz, Q., Napier, J., Fido, R. J., Shewry, P. R. & Paredes-López, O. (2000). Overexpression, purification, and *in vitro* refolding of the 11S globulin from Amaranth seed in *Escherichia coli*. *J. Agric. Food Chem.*, *48*, 5249–5255.

Paredes-López, O., Mora-Escobedo, R. & Ordorica-Falomir, C. (1988). Isolation of amaranth protein. *Lebensm Wis U-Technol.*, *21*, 59–61.

Peña-Ramos, E. & Xiong, Y. (2003). Whey and soy protein hydrolysates inhibit lipid oxidation in cooked pork patties. *Meat Sci.*, *64*, 259–263.

Petruccelli, S. & Añón, M. C. (1995). Thermal aggregation of soy protein isolates. *J. Agric. Food Chem.*, *43*, 3035–3041.

Plate, A. Y. A. & Arêas, J. A. G. (2002). Cholesterol-lowering effect of extruded amaranth (*Amaranthus caudatus* L.) in hypercholesterolemic rabbits. *Food Chem.*, *76*, 1-6.

Quirós, A., Ramos, M., Muguerza, B., Delgado, M. A., Miguel, M., Aleixandre, A. & Recio, I. (2007). Identification of novel antihypertensive peptides in milk fermented with *Enterococcus faecalis*. *Int. Dairy J.*, *17*, 33–41.

Rascón-Cruz, Q., Sinagawa-García, S., Osuna-Castro, J. A., Bohorova, N. & Paredes-López, O. (2004). Accumulation, assembly, and digestibility of amarantin expressed in transgenic tropical maize. *Theor. Appl. Genet.*, *108*, 335-342.

Rezaei, J., Rouzbehan, Y. &Fazaeli, H. (2009). Nutritive value of fresh and ensiled amaranth (*Amaranthus hypochondriacus*) treated with different levels of molasses. *Anim. Feed Sci. Techol.*, *151*, 153-160.

Rodríguez Patino, J. M., MiñonesConde, J., Millán Linares, H., Pedroche Jiménez, J. J., Carrera Sánchez, C., Pizones, V. & Millán Rodríguez, F. (2007). Interfacial and foaming properties of enzyme-induced hydrolysis of sunflower protein isolate. *Food Hydrocolloids*, *21*, 782–793.

Romero-Zepeda, H. & Paredes-López, O. (1996). Isolation and characterization of amarantin and the 11S amaranth seed globulin. *J. Food Biochem.*, *19*, 329-339.

Rooke, L., Békés, F., Fido, R., Barro, F., Gras, P., Tatham, A. S., Barcelo, P., Lazzeri, P. & Shewry, P. R. (1999). Overexpression of a gluten protein in transgenic wheat results in greatly increased dough strength. *J. Cereal Sci.*, *30*, 115-120.

Rosales-Mendoza, S., Paz-Maldonado, L. M. T., Govea-Alonso, D. O. & Korban, S. S. (2013). Engineering production of antihypertensive peptides in plants. *Plant Cell Tiss. Org. Cult.*, *112*, 159-169.

Sacks, F. M. & Campos, H. (2010). Dietary therapy in hypertension. *N. Engl. J. Med.*, *362*, 2102–2112.

Santos-Ballardo, D. U., Germán-Báez, L. J., Cruz-Mendívil, A., Fuentes-Gutiérrez, C. I., Milán-Carrillo, J., Reyes-Moreno, C. & Valdez-Ortiz, A. (2013). Expression of the acidic-subunit of amarantin, carring the antihypertensive biopeptides VY, in cell suspension cultures Nicotianatabacum NT1. *Plant Cell Tiss. Organ. Cult.*, *113*, 315-322.

Scilingo, A. A., Molina Ortiz, S. E., Martínez, E. N. & Añón, M. C. (2002). Amaranth protein isolates modified by hydrolytic and thermal treatments. Relationship between structure and solubility. *Food Res. Int.*, *35*, 855-862.

Segura-Nieto, M., Barba de la Rosa, A. P. & Paredes-López, O. (1994). Biochemistry of amaranth proteins. In: Paredes-López, O. (Ed.): *Amaranth: Biology, Chemistry and Technology*, Chapter 6. Boca Raton: CRC Press.

Seppo, L., Jauhiainen, T., Poussa, T. & Korpela, R. (2003). A fermented milk high in bioac- tive peptides has a blood pressure lowering effect in hypertensive subjects. *Am. J. Clin. Nutr.*, *77*, 326–330.

Shewry, P. R. (1998). Manipulation of seed storage proteins. In:Lindsey, K.(Ed.): *Transgenic Plant Research*, Chapter 8. Harwood Academic Publishers: Reading, UK, pp135-149.

Shewry, P. R., Napier, J. A. & Tatham, A. S. (1995). Seed storage proteins: Structure and biosynthesis. *Plant Cell, 7*, 945-956.

Sibbel, A. (2007). The sustainability of functional foods. *Soc. Sci. Med.*, *64*, 554–561.

Silva-Sánchez, C., Barba de La Rosa, A. P., León-Galván, M. F., De Lumen, B. O., De León-Rodríguez, A. & González de Mejía, E. (2008). Bioactive peptides in amaranth (*Amaranthus hypochondriacus*) seed. *J. Agric. Food Chem.*, *56*, 1233–40.

Sinagawa-García, S. R., Rascón-Cruz, Q., Valdez-Ortiz, A., Medina-Godoy, S., Escobar- Gutiérrez, A. & Paredes-López, O. (2004). Safety assessment by *in vitro* digestibility and allergenicity of genetically modified maize with an amaranth 11S globulin. *J. Agric. Food Chem. 52*, 2709–2714.

Sindhu, A. S., Zheng, Z. & Murai, N. (1997). The pea seed storage protein legumin was synthesized, processed, and accumulated stably in transgenic rice endosperm. *Plant Sci.*, *130*, 189-196.

Srivastava, R. & Roy, B. K. (2013). Proteomic analysis of different extracts from amaranth (*Amaranthus tricolor*) grains. *Asian J. Pharm. Clin. Res.*, *6*, 37-39.

Stallknecht, G. F. & Schultz-Schaeffer, J. R. (1993). Amaranth rediscovered. In: *New crops*. New York: Wiley, pp. 211–218.

Stöger, E., Parker, M., Christou, P. & Casey, R. (2001). Pea legumin overexpressed in wheat endosperm assembles into an ordered paracrystalline matrix. *Plant Physiol.*, *125*, 1732–1742.

Svirskis, A. (2003). Investigation of amaranth cultivation and utilization in Lithuania. *Agron. Res.*, *1*, 253–264.

Teutonico, R. A. & Knorr, D. (1985). Amaranth: composition, properties and applications of a rediscovered food crop. *Food Technol.*, *39*, 49–60.

Tiengo, A., Faria, M. & Netto, F. M. (2009). Characterization and ACE-Inhibitory activity of amaranth proteins. *J. Food Sci.*, *74*, H121–H126.

Tironi, V. A. & Añón, M. C. (2010). Amaranth proteins as a source of antioxidant peptides: Effect of proteolysis. *Food Res. Int.*, *43*, 315-322.

Utsumi, S., Damodaran, S. & Kinsella, J. E. (1984). Heat-induced interactions between soybean proteins: Preferential association of 11S basic subunits and β-subunits of 7S. *J. Agric. Food Chem.*, *32*, 1406-1412.

Valdez-Ortiz, A., Medina-Godoy, S., Valverde, M. & Paredes-López, O. (2007). Transgenic tropical maize generated by the direct transformation of the embryo-scutellum by *A. tumefaciens*. *Plant Cell Tiss. Org. Cult.*, *91*, 201–214.

Valdez-Ortiz, A., Rascón-Cruz, Q., Medina-Godoy, S., Sinagawa- García, S. R., Valverde-González, M. E. & Paredes-López, O. (2005). One-step purification and structural characterization of a recombinant His-tag 11S globulin expressed in transgenic tobacco. *J. Biotechnol.*, *115*, 413–423.

Vecchi, B. & Añón, M. C. (2009). ACE inhibitory tetrapeptides from *Amaranthus hypochondriacus* 11S globulin. *Phytochemistry*, *70*, 864-870.

Weber, A. (1990). Amaranth grain production guide. Emmaus, PA: Rodale Press. p. 28.

Wei, Y. & Lee, H. (2002). Oxidative stress, mitochondrial DNA mutation, and impairment of antioxidant enzymes in aging. *Exp. Biol. Med.*, *227*, 671–682.

Wright, D.J. (1988). The seed globulins—part II. In: Hudson, B.J.F. (Ed.), *Developments in Food Proteins*. Elsevier Applied Science, London, pp. 119–177.

Yang, S. H., Moran, D. L., Jia, H. W., Bicar, E. H., Lee, M. & Scott, M. P. (2002). Expression of a synthetic porcine alpha-lactalbumin gene in the kernels of transgenic maize. *Transgenic Res.*, *11*, 11–20.

Yokoyama, S. (2003). Protein expression systems for structural genomics and proteomics. *Curr. Opin. Chem. Biol.*, *7*, 39–43.

Yu LG, Milton JD, Fernig DG, & Rhodes JM. (2001). Opposite effects on human colon cancer cell proliferation of two dietary Thomsen-Friedenreich antigen-binding lectins. *J. Cell. Physiol.*, *186*, 282–7.

Zheng, B., Matsumura, Y. & Mori, T. (1993). of molecular forces to rheological and structural properties of legumin gels from broad beans. *Biosci. Biotechnol. Biochem.*, *57*, 1257–1260.

In: Globulins
Editor: Sheila D. Milford

ISBN: 978-1-63117-781-1
© 2014 Nova Science Publishers, Inc.

Chapter 4

SEED STORAGE GLOBULINS: THEIR DESCENT FROM BACTERIAL ANCESTORS AND MECHANISMS OF DEGRADATION

Andrei D. Shutov[1] and Karl A. Wilson[2,]*
[1]Laboratory of Plant Biochemistry, Moldova State University,
Chişinău, Republic of Moldova
[2]Department of Biological Sciences,
State University of New York at Binghamton, NY, US

ABSTRACT

Legumin and vicilin are seed storage globulins characteristic of spermatophytes. Subunits of both the globulins are composed of homologous N-terminal and C-terminal domains. A β-barrel of eight antiparallel β-strands conjoined with a group of α-helices represents the structural basis of the domains. Legumin and vicilin share tertiary and quaternary structures with homologous bacterial two-domain oxalate decarboxylases that are regarded as the most ancient two-domain progenitors of seed storage globulins. A green alga two-domain protein highly homologous to bacterial oxalate decarboxylases reflects features of the most ancient plant ancestor of seed storage globulins. The diversification of the storage globulin evolutionary pathway into legumin and vicilin branches occurred at the level of non-seed plants like club

---

* Corresponding author: kwilson@binghamton.edu.

moss and fern. The development of legumin/vicilin-like proteins into spermatophyte legumin and vicilin consisted of insertion of hydrophilic sequence regions specifically extended inside the domain structures of genuine storage globulins. These extensions are regarded as specific targets for immediate proteolytic attack in legumin and vicilin structures.

Two distinct mechanisms of proteolysis are responsible for the degradation of seed storage globulins in germinating seeds and *in vitro*, limited and extensive (one-by-one) proteolyses. The limited proteolysis is restricted to cleavage of a limited number of peptide bonds specifically susceptible to proteolytic attack. In contrast, the extensive proteolysis is unlimited and consists of one-by-one deep degradation of protein molecules. The separate analysis of the kinetics of limited and extensive proteolyses *in vitro* detected two pathways of degradation of seed storage globulins. In the first, exclusively limited proteolysis occurs at the beginning of the reaction when the native protein substrate is inaccessible to one-by-one proteolysis. In this case, structural alterations of the protein substrate due to the limited proteolysis are expected to bring about its susceptibility to unlimited degradation by the one-by-one mechanism. In the second pathway, the packing density of a storage globulin molecule is relatively low, resulting in susceptibility of the native protein substrate to one-by-one proteolysis. In this case limited and one-by-one proteolyses occur in parallel independent of each other from the very beginning of the reaction. On the basis of comparison of the patterns of *in vitro* and *in vivo* proteolysis it was suggested that both the pathways of massive storage globulin degradation do occur during germination and seedling growth.

INTRODUCTION

In all spermatophytes, only two kinds of seed proteins have served, lacking other functions, as nutritional reservoirs for early seedling growth [1]. These are legumin and vicilin, also called 11S and 7S globulins, respectively. Both proteins are accumulated during seed maturation and are subsequently completely degraded when the seeds germinate and seedlings start to grow. Two general mechanisms are responsible for such a temporal separation of storage globulin synthesis and degradation [2]. First, the globulins are transported into membrane-bounded storage compartments to protect them from cytoplasmic proteinases; their massive degradation is usually catalyzed by proteinases synthesized *de novo* during seed germination and seedling growth. Second, primary and higher order structures of storage globulins are specifically adapted to provide their stability before germination, followed by controlled degradation after germination.

Legumin and vicilin subunits are both composed of homologous N-terminal and C-terminal domains. The structure specific to storage globulin domains can be exemplified by the most conserved C-terminal domain of *Glycine max* legumin 1OD5 [3] (Figure 1A). A β-barrel of eight antiparallel β-strands *BCDEFGHI* represents a fundamental module of the domain structures. The core module is further extended by the additional antiparallel β-strands *A'*, *A* and *J, J'*. An additional strand *Z* in both vicilin domains [4] and in the C-terminal domain of legumin stabilizes the inter-domain interactions. The sequences between the strands *J* and *J'* form α-helices *h1-h3* and the additional α-helix *h0* is formed between the strands *A* and *B*. In vicilins, the additional α-helix *h4* is formed between the N- and C-terminal domains [4].

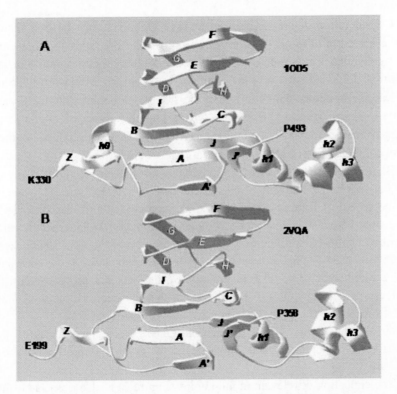

Figure 1. Ribbon diagrams of the superimposed but shown separately backbone structures of C-terminal domains of legumin 1OD5 from *Glycine max* (A) and OD 2VQA from cyanobacteria *Synechocystis sp.* (B). A least-squares fit produced an RMSD of 1.47 Å between the legumin and OD using 235 C$^\alpha$ atoms from their full-length superimposed two-domain subunit sequences.

The seed storage proteins are an important source of nutrition for both mankind and our livestock. Therefore, various aspects of the biochemistry and molecular biology of both legumin and vicilin have been intensively studied, including the problem of real and potential allergenicity of storage globulins. In this chapter, we consider the evolutionary pathway of formation of storage globulin structure. Further, the mechanisms of storage protein proteolytic degradation, especially as related to the structure of these proteins, are analyzed.

ORIGIN AND EVOLUTIONARY PATHWAY OF SEED STORAGE GLOBULINS

Consideration of the structure of storage globulins must be first focused on the basic cupin motif (a β-barrel of antiparallel β-strands [5]) present in their molecules. Thousands of other proteins containing cupin motifs in their known or predicted structures are available in databases. Moreover, a number of these are bi-cupins containing, like the storage globulins, doubled β-barrel motifs in their sequences. However, only a limited number of bi-cupins and cupins share the domain structure characteristic of storage globulins, i.e. the β-barrel conjoined C-terminally with a group of α-helices.

BLAST searches followed by phylogenetic analysis (Figure 2) created rich collections of relevant bi-cupins divided into three types: 1) Genuine storage globulins from spermatophytes, 2) Separate legumin-like and vicilin-like proteins from the club moss *Selaginella moellendorffii* and also the earlier described vicilin-like protein caa91187 from the fern *Matteuccia struthiopteris* spores [6-8], 3) Highly conserved oxalate decarboxylases (ODs) available from a number of bacterial taxa including cyanobacteria, proteobacteria and firmicutes, and fungal ODs. A fourth type of these bi-cupins hitherto available only from the green alga *Coccomyxa subellipsoidea* (eie22877) is a two-domain protein highly similar to bacterial ODs. Selected sequences of plant and bacterial bi-cupins aligned together with the green alga protein are shown in Figure 3.

The collection of relevant mono-cupins (Figure 2) is also rich: 1) Genuine germins from monocots and dicots, and germin-like proteins from gymnosperms, mosses and club moss, 2) Spherulins from *Physarum polycephalum* (Amoebozoa) and fungi, and spherulin-like proteins from *Ectocarpus siliculosus* (Stramenopiles), and 3) Bacterial single-domain ODs.

The primary and tertiary structures of the seed storage globulin domains share a high degree of similarity with bacterial ODs [9] (see Figure 1) as well as with germins [10]. Therefore, two alternative evolutionary pathways have previously been proposed, i.e. that the two-domain storage globulins have either evolved directly from bacterial two-domain ODs [11], or that they descended from an ancestral germin-like protein by duplication of its single domain [12].

Phylogenetic analysis of sequences from all of the above collections of mono-cupins and bi-cupins revealed equal relation of germin/spherulin and storage globulin branches to bacterial two-domain ODs (Figure 2). A similar result was obtained earlier when the β-barrel sequences of both storage globulin domains have been involved in phylogenetic analysis [9]. Thus, both the trees could not discriminate between the above alternative scenarios of storage globulin origin.

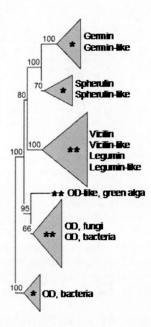

Figure 2. Phylogenetic analysis of a representative collections of mono-cupin (*) and bi-cupin (**) sequences containing a β-barrel C-terminally extended by a group of helices. The tree was constructed using TREECON [13]. Sequence region analyzed is restricted to C-terminal domains of bi-cupins and the domain of mono-cupins (167 alignment positions covering the entire domain sequences, strands Z - J', see Figure 1). Numbers along the branches refer to bootstrap values (% from 1000 replicates). Bacterial single-domain ODs were used as outgroups.

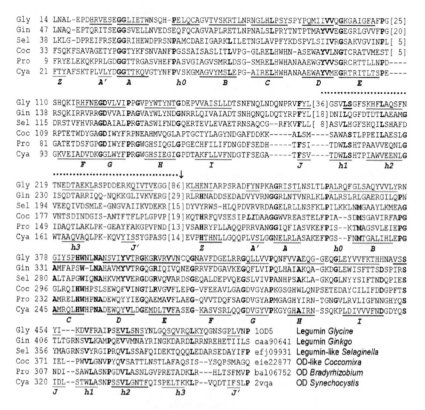

Figure 3. Domain sequences of bacterial ODs, legumins and the green alga OD-like protein. Residues in bold indicate identities shared at least by four sequences. Numbers in square brackets indicate positions and sizes of three variable regions extended in legumin sequences (a loop between the β-strands *E* and *F*, the β-barrel/helix junction and the inter-domain linker) [2] omitted from the alignment and further analysis. Underlined residues correspond to 2D structures in the 1OD5 and 2VQA. Leu-Ile residues shown in bold italics correspond to the predicted splicing site in *Coccomixa* eie22888 gene sequence. An arrow ↓ indicates position of processing site in legumin sequences. A dotted line above the alignment indicate sequence region detached from soybean legumin subunits by *in vitro* and *in vivo* limited proteolysis [14].

Nevertheless, the origin of two-domain storage globulin structure from bacterial two-domain ODs, rather than from the single-domain germins, seems to be most probable. Indeed, the *two-domain* OD-like protein detected in green alga can be evaluated as reflecting features of the most ancient plant ancestor of the *two-domain* storage globulins (Figure 2). Additionally, both storage globulin and OD structures are stabilized by β-strands *Z*, *A'* and *J'* that are lacking in germins. Moreover, in contrast to similarly sized legumins and the most related group of bacterial ODs, germin as well as spherulin sequences are specifically extended N-terminally. Taken together, these circumstances allow analyzing the storage globulin evolutionary pathway separately from single-domain cupins, although they are related.

An evolutionary tree based on the aligned amino acid sequences of storage globulin N- and C-terminal domains and those of all other types of related two-domain proteins (see above) places the green alga (eie22877) and club moss (efjJ19431 and efj18494) sequences as successive evolutionary intermediates between bacterial ODs and storage globulin-like proteins (Figure 4). It should be mentioned that the second green alga protein (eie22888) is truncated N-terminally.

According to the endosymbiotic theory, the chloroplasts in eukaryotic algae and higher plants have evolved from cyanobacterial ancestors via endosymbiosis. A plethora of genes have been shown to have been transferred from the genome of the cyanobacterial endosymbiont to the host nuclear genome [15]. Therefore, it was tempting to speculate that the high degree of similarity of cyanobacterial ODs and seed storage globulins at the levels of primary and higher order structures (Figure 1 and 3) can be regarded as an evidence for the involvement of endosymbiosis in the evolution of seed storage globulins [9]. However, only three OD genes are detectable in the numerous cyanobacterial genomes sequenced (PCC 6312, 6803 and 7942) although many hundreds of OD sequences are available in different bacterial taxa. It seems likely that the OD genes rarely present in cyanobacterial species appeared due to a horizontal gene transfer from other bacteria. If so, the OD-like primary structure of eie22877 might be directly inherited from a group of proteobacteria whose ODs specifically cluster with cyanobacterial ODs (Figure 4). In a similar way, the structure of fungal ODs probably was inherited from the other specific group of bacterial ODs, including 1UW8 from *Bacillus subtilis* (Figure 4). The mechanism of this direct inheritance (no intermediates are available in databases) is unclear for both the cases. In this context, it should be mentioned that ten percent of proteins in plant plastids have been recently estimated as derived from bacteria via a horizontal gene transfer [16]. Possibly, the OD-like structure of the green alga proteins (and fungal ODs as well) was inherited from a specific group of bacterial ODs by the same mechanism. The question is whether such a single-shot event of the gene transfer was sufficiently ancient to be inherited in genes from other green alga species that would represent still missing links between the green alga and non-seed plants (i.e. antecedent to the strongly storage globulin-like club moss protein efj19431).

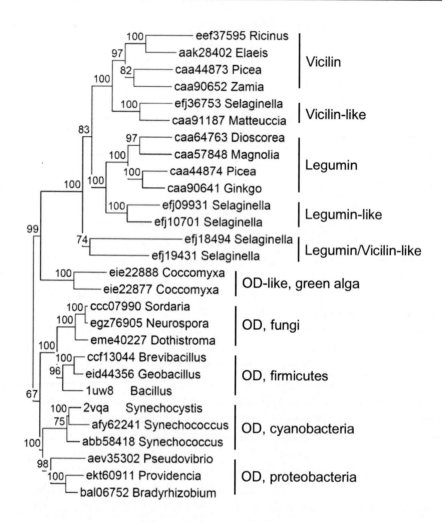

Figure 4. Hypothetical evolutionary pathways of seed storage globulins. The tree was constructed using TREECON [13]. Sequence regions subjected to analysis correspond to the sum of N-terminal and C-terminal domains of storage globulins and other bi-cupins (324 alignment positions). Numbers along the branches refer to bootstrap values (% from 1000 replicates). Bacterial sequences have been used as outgroups.

The diversification of storage globulins into separate legumin and vicilin branches occurred at the level of non-seed plants (Figure 4). The process was accompanied with gain of four (legumin) and five (vicilin) introns. All these introns are located in highly conserved gene regions matching in aligned amino acid sequences of legumin and vicilin [17, 18], and legumin-/vicilin-like proteins. Three kinds of introns of identical positions and phases are detectable (Figure 5): 1) three introns in both storage globulins and in both legumin-like and vicilin-like genes (two in the N-domain, one in the C-domain), 2) the fourth intron specific of legumins/legumin-like proteins (in the C-domain), and 3) two introns specific of vicilin/vicilin-like proteins (one in each of the N- and C-domains). Positions and phases of the third and fourth introns in the *Selaginella* efj18494 gene, estimated as an intermediate (Figure 4), coincide with those of legumins/legumin-like proteins; the efj18494 gene lacks the third intron specific of vicilins/vicilin-like proteins. Moreover, in some alternative alignments the efj18494 sequence tends to join legumin/legumin-like cluster (data not shown). These circumstances indicate that legumin-like rather than vicilin-like structure is characteristic of the efj18494 gene expected to be most ancient together with the *Selaginella* efj19431 gene (Figure 4). Therefore, the formation of vicilin/vicilin-like gene structure can be estimated as more recent event consisting of gain of an additional intron specific of vicilin/vicilin-like proteins and a shift of the fifth intron downstream from its position in legumin/legumin-like genes (Figure 5). The exon/intron structure of vicilin genes is stable in all spermatophytes, whereas the fourth legumin intron was lost at the beginning of angiosperm diversification [19].

The positions of introns detected in the green alga OD-like genes eie22877 and eie22888, and in *Selaginella* legumin/vicilin-like gene efj19431 are different from those shown in Figure 5. Hence, the presumed development of these genes into storage globulin-like genes should be accompanied with loss of the primary introns and gain of new ones specific of storage globulin genes.

The evolution of legumin/vicilin-like proteins into the genuine legumins and vicilins of the spermatophytes included two major kinds of events. The first specific to the genuine legumins involves the generation of the inter-domain Asn-specific processing site (Figure 3) and the formation of an inter-domain disulfide bond. The second event was the insertion of hydrophilic regions within the domain structure of genuine legumins (N-terminal domain *EF* loop and β-barrel/α-helix junction, see Figure 3) and vicilins (C-terminal domain *EF* loop). These extensions, which are lacking in storage globulin-like proteins, may be regarded as targets for the proteolytic attack initiating protein mobilization during seed germination [2]. Two additional regions are extended in storage globulin sequences: the N-terminal region of convicilin-like vicilins and the inter-domain linker in both vicilins and especially legumins [20, 21].

Storage and mobilization can be regarded as antagonistic functional constraints that drove the evolution of storage globulin primary and tertiary structures [2]. Naturally, two questions relevant to the storage function of seed globulins arise. First, why was the bacterial OD structure selected as a suitable template to create genuine storage globulins? Second, how are those regions that have been specifically extended in storage globulins protected against premature cleavages?

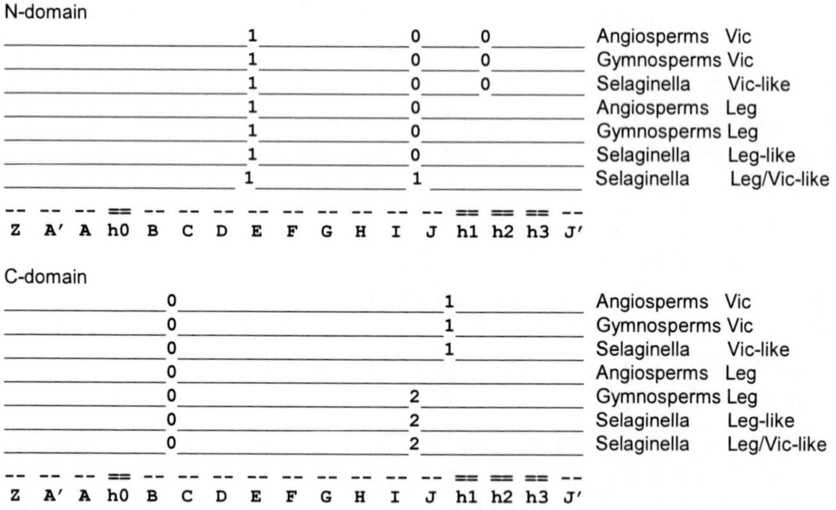

N-domain

		1		0	0		Angiosperms	Vic
		1		0	0		Gymnosperms	Vic
		1		0	0		Selaginella	Vic-like
		1		0			Angiosperms	Leg
		1		0			Gymnosperms	Leg
		1		0			Selaginella	Leg-like
		1		1			Selaginella	Leg/Vic-like

```
-- -- -- ≡≡ -- -- -- -- -- -- -- -- -- ≡≡ ≡≡ ≡≡ --
Z  A' A  h0 B  C  D  E  F  G  H  I  J  h1 h2 h3 J'
```

C-domain

	0			1		Angiosperms	Vic
	0			1		Gymnosperms	Vic
	0			1		Selaginella	Vic-like
	0					Angiosperms	Leg
	0		2			Gymnosperms	Leg
	0		2			Selaginella	Leg-like
	0		2			Selaginella	Leg/Vic-like

```
-- -- -- ≡≡ -- -- -- -- -- -- -- -- -- ≡≡ ≡≡ ≡≡ --
Z  A' A  h0 B  C  D  E  F  G  H  I  J  h1 h2 h3 J'
```

Figure 5. Schematic presentation of the exon/intron structures of vicilin (Vic) and legumin (Leg) genes and the genes of their ancestors. The scheme is projected into aligned sequences of the N-terminal and C-terminal domains (Figure 3). Numbers indicate positions and phases of introns. Positions of the first and second introns in *Selaginella* legumin/vicilin-like efj18494 gene are shifted from those common to legumin/legumin-like and vicilin/vicilin-like genes (by three bp upstream and by one bp downstream, respectively).

The β-barrel conjoined with a group of α-helices as a core of the germin domain exemplifies the structures of vicilin N-terminal and legumin C-terminal domains lacking hydrophilic extensions, as well as the structures of both domains of the bacterial ODs. Notably, germin is extremely resistant to any proteolytic attack [22].

It seems likely that the β-barrel/α-helix structure was selected by the evolution as the most suitable to provide stability of storage globulin domains during reserve accumulation in seed development.

Legumin

```
                    EF loop
QQGKGIFGMIYPG  CPSTFEEPQQPQ------------------------------------QRGQSSRPQD  RHQKIYNFREGDL  1fxz       Glycine
AQGKGALGVAIPG  CPETFEEPQEQSNRRG-----------------------------------SRSQKQQLQD  SHQKIRHFNEGDV  bad72975   Glycine
QQGKALVGISAPG  CPESFHSGQRSPRSFE----------------------------------EGSSQQFQTD  SHNKLYRVRQGDI  caa64763   Dioscorea
QQGRGLLGITYPG  CAETYRSRGQPQRTGGEQ---------------------------------QQQRGESISD  QHQKIHRIRRGDI  caa57848   Magnolia
VRGEGRLGIVFPG  CPETFRDHSSFQGRSRRRSEGR-------------------------------REEEEEEEED  SSQKVRRVRRGDV  caa44874   Picea
VEGEGRLGVVFPG  CPETFQSSTS-----------------------------------------RGGEGQQSQE  RSQKIRRVRRGDV  caa90641   Ginkgo
VRGSAKVGVINPL  ADKII-----------------------------------------------DRSTVFHVRAGDA  efj09931  Selaginella

                    β-barrel/α-helix junction
ENQLDQMPRRFYL  AGNQEQEFLKYQQEQGGHQSQKG----------------------KHQQEEENEG  GSILSGFTLEFLL  1fxz       Glycine
DLNNEPSLRTFLL  AGNFQEQSSSAGQQYEQ-----------------------------EKDPQRSSPR  DNIIRAFDQQMIS  caa64763   Dioscorea
DFNSDQRPRSFYF  AGGSPQQQQGQQQRR-------------------------------EGQHQQMEGE  ENIIQAFNENILA  caa57848   Magnolia
DTSSSRSYRPFSL  AGPGSSSRRE--------------------------------------EGEGEGRGIG  SNIFAGFSTRTLA  caa44874   Picea
DTSNDQTYRPFYL  AGSAPSGA--------------------------------------QKAAGATSIG  DNILQGFDTDTLA  caa90641   Ginkgo
VAETRNRFKVFLL  AGGKKE----------------------------------------NY  ASVLHGFSKQILS  efj09931  Selaginella

                    Inter-domain linker                          ↓
GEDKGAIVTVKGG  LSVIKPPTDEQQQRPQEEEEEEEDEKPQCKGKDKHCQRPRGSQSKSRRNGIDETICTM  RLRHNIGQTSSPD  1fxz       Glycine
SDKRGHIIRVEQG  LSHVWPEEQEEQEECMDEARPKESQFA--------------------NGLEEAICYA  RVQYNLDRPEERP  caa64763   Dioscorea
NDDRGYIVKVKRG  EMSMVRPDEEAEDEEQYQQGRR----------------------------NGFEEVYCNM  RVNHYMDNPRENP  caa57848   Magnolia
NQQSRLFARVERG  QRLSLPGPRSRSRSPYERETERDDVAGGLQGYYSSGDE----------NGVEELVCPL  RVKHNADNPEDNP  caa44873   Picea
NQKKGLIVKVERG  LRMPGPPSDDYERERREG----------------------------NNVEEFYCSM  RLRHNADDSEDDS  caa90641   Ginkgo
GNGVAIIKVDEKR  KMSLP-----------------------------------------GNTHSNNIFI  DYVYRWSHLQPHL  efj09931  Selaginella
```

Vicilin

```
                    Inter-domain linker
RLQESVIVEISKK  QIRELSKH------------------------------------AKSSSRKTIS  SEDKPFNLRSRDP  1uik       Glycine
TQKQEAIVKASKE  QIQAMTHRDQEG---------------------------------GTIWPFGGES  SGAPFNLLHKRPV  eef37595   Ricinus
KQNKGAIIQASQE  QIKEMSR--------------------------------------GSEGRSWPFG  ESRRPFNLFHKRP  aak28402   Elaeis
GHKSGVIIHANEE  QIREMMRKR------------------------------------GFSAGSMSAP  EHPKPFNLRNQKP  caa44873   Picea
GFNRGAIIRVSRE  QMERLS---------------------------------------RGRIKGFGGS  EEPQPFNLLYRNP  caa90652   Zamia
SQTQGPIIYFSGR  NESKRGDAAGLGLGKSLTDM-------------------------LDRYIGLPTD  SGKKPYNLFKEKA  caa91187   Matteuccia

                    EF loop
ANIELVGIKEQQQ  RQQ-----------------------------------------QEEQPLEVRK  YRAELSEQDIFVI  1uik       Glycine
GYMEMACPHLSGG  SEH-----------------------------------------QGRRGQTYGR  VRSRLRPGTVFIV  eef37595   Ricinus
GDVQIVCPHISRQ  QEEGRRGREEEEGRGRQEGREEEEEEEE----------------QQQRGQHYRR  VESKVSCGTTFIV  aak28402   Elaeis
GRIEMACPHLGQH  GWSSPRE-------------------------------------RGDQDITYQR  VWAKLRTGSVYIV  caa44873   Picea
GILELVRPQEQEQ  QQ------------------------------------------QQQQGPTYQK  LRANLNPGTVFLT  caa90652   Zamia
GETQIVYPNGSAA  --------------------------------------------ATQRVSEGSVFFV  caa91187   Matteuccia
```

```
                    N-terminal extension
                              VEEEEECEEGQIPRPRPQHPERERQQHGEKEEDEG
             EQPRPFPFPRPRQPHQEEEHEQKEEHEWHRKEEKHGGKGSEEEQDEREHPRPHQPHQK
             EEEKHEWQHKQEKHQGKESEEEEEDQDEDEEQDKESQESEGSESQREPRRHKNKNPFH  FNSKRFQTLFKNQ  baa74452   Glycine
                              QATTDPELKQCKHQCKVQRQYGEDQKRQCMRRCE
             EYYREKERERERREGEGEGEGEGGGRGSSGHREEDDWDVSSTTDPEKRLRECQRQCERQ
             EGQQRTLCRRRCQESYERERERREEGGRGEREHGREKGGGRGGKEEETNEEAEENPYV  FDTDQFTEKVRTE  eef37595   Ricinus
                              VSATLTFSATTE
             DPKQRLERCKQECRESRQGERQERRCVSQCEERYERERRREQEERKGQGEERGRREEPE
             KRLEECRRECREQAERRERRECEKRCEEEYKEHRGRSKDKEEGEEGRGEKRRESDPYF  FDEESFLHRVRTE  aak28402   Elaeis
```

Figure 6. Extended hydrophilic regions of storage globulin subunits (boxed part of the figure) specialized as targets for limited proteolysis usually lack Asn residues. As a rule, the few Asn residues found in some storage globulins are usually located in close proximity to the structurally ordered elements (underlined) and thereby are protected against attack by Asn-specific legumain [2]. All Asn residues are printed in bold. An arrow ↓ indicates position of Asn-specific processing site in legumin subunits.

In developing seeds, legumin and vicilin are co-localized with each other as well as with the active Asn-specific proteinase legumain that catalyzes prolegumin processing shown in Figure 3 and 6. Thus, the potentially susceptible extensions in both legumin and vicilin structures, which are usually disordered [4, 21] and highly variable in size and sequence [2], should be structurally accessible to legumain attack. However, an extensive analysis of storage globulin sequences revealed that all the five kinds of the extensions usually lack Asn residues (Figure 6) [2]. Hence, functional (i.e. the protection against premature cleavage), rather than higher order structural constraints, have determined the evolution of the primary structure of the extensions specific to genuine storage globulins.

The above information describes structural relation of storage globulins to their storage function. The structural relation of storage globulins to their further function during seed germination and seedling growth is analyzed below.

STRUCTURALLY RELATED MECHANISMS OF STORAGE GLOBULIN DEGRADATION

Limited ("zipper") and extensive (one-by-one) proteolyses as mechanisms responsible for proteolytic degradation of native proteins [23-25] are generalized in Table 1. The limited proteolysis can be exemplified by the well known processing of protein precursors (e.g., enzyme activation). A site-specific limited proteolysis, which resembles proteolytic processing, occurs when the degradation of storage globulins starts during seed germination or *in vitro* [2, 26]. Rapid limited mobilization of a susceptible part of protein reserves (namely, the extended hydrophilic regions, Figure 6) prior to their massive degradation might be a simple explanation for the functional role of storage globulin limited proteolysis [27]. However, as it was hypothesized previously [26] and supported by further experimental data described below, an additional import of limited proteolysis exists. *In vitro* as well as *in vivo* degradation patterns of phaseolin (vicilin) from common bean (*Phaseolus vulgaris*) seeds is the best support for this assumption.

Table 1. General features of idealized limited and one-by-one proteolyses

Limited proteolysis	One-by-one proteolysis
Protein weight concentration is reduced only due to lowering of the molecular mass of the substrate	Protein weight concentration is reduced only due to disappearance of the substrate molecules
Protein molar concentration remains constant along the reaction	Molecular mass of the residual protein remains constant along the reaction
Process stops after successive exhaustion of susceptible sites in protein substrate	Process stops after exhaustion of protein molecules
Protein remainder is a relatively stable high-molecular-mass product	The one-by-one proteolysis is a pseudo-first order reaction [24, 25]

In vitro hydrolysis of phaseolin by numerous proteinases (trypsin, chymotrypsin, papain and pepsin, see [28, 29] for references) is restricted to limited proteolysis. Intriguingly, the individual action of both the endogenous enzymes responsible for massive degradation of phaseolin *in vivo* (papain-like proteinase CPPh [30] and Asn-specific legumain [31]) is restricted *in vitro* to only limited proteolysis.

However, when phaseolin is first treated the legumain, limited proteolysis generated by this enzyme renders the phaseolin susceptible to one-by-one proteolysis by the papain-like proteinase [28]. Hence, the combined limited proteolysis generates structural alterations of phaseolin, and thereby triggers its subsequent massive degradation.

Thus, the involvement of two different enzymes in limited proteolysis reactions is needed to convert phaseolin into a degradable form. Therefore, in the case of phaseolin, the regulatory role of the limited proteolysis is unequivocal.

However, such a pattern of the extensive proteolysis of a storage globulin is specific to this species. Usually, single enzymes catalyze both the limited and one-by-one proteolyses of vicilin and legumin [26, 27]. In these cases, it is thus unclear as to whether limited proteolysis is needed before the extensive protein degradation can take place, or whether both of the processes occur independently, in parallel, from the very beginning of the reaction. To examine this question, we used a strategy described below.

The Strategy for Separate Analysis of Kinetics of Limited and One-by-One Proteolyses

Limited proteolysis is the sum of one to several reactions of successively decreasing rates. In contrast, the rate of one-by-one proteolysis is limited by the rate of cleavage of the first peptide bond in each protein molecule [23]. Consequently, it may be regarded as a first-order reaction. Therefore, the linearity of the plot log P vs. t (where P is protein weight concentration and t is the reaction time) is characteristic of the exclusive one-by-one proteolysis [24, 25].

During mixed-type proteolysis, when limited and one-by-one proteolyses occur simultaneously, the decrease of P value is determined by simultaneous decline in the molecular mass M of the protein and its molar concentration (Table 1). At each time point of the reaction, the relative decrease of protein weight concentration due exclusively to limited proteolysis is equal to 100%-

M%. When these values are added to the relative protein weight concentration P determined experimentally in the reaction mixture, the resulting sum (100%-M%)+P% plotted vs. the reaction time t describes the kinetics of an exclusively one-by-one proteolysis [14]. Naturally, relative molecular mass values M% plotted vs. the reaction time t describe the kinetics of an exclusively limited proteolysis.

In this way, the kinetics of limited and one-by-one proteolyses can be analyzed separately on the basis of the values of the molecular mass M and the weight concentration P of the residual protein determined experimentally during the reaction [14].

In experiments described below in detail, the M values were taken to be equal to the number-average molecular mass of the residual protein produced in the course of proteolysis, calculated using the molecular masses of polypeptides separated by SDS-PAGE and the relative intensity of the respective bands. The P values were taken to be represented by the amounts of trichloroacetic acid-insoluble part of the reaction mixture.

Cleavage points (or cleavage regions) were identified on the basis of the time course of formation and apparent molecular masses of polypeptide fragments detected by SDS-page as well as on the basis the N-terminal sequencing and mass spectrometry of the proteolysis products.

Papain-like proteinases of low specificity are the major enzymes responsible for *in vivo* degradation of legumin and vicilin [27]. Therefore, papain from papaya latex has been used as probe enzyme in the experiments described below in detail. Papain exhibits broad specificity, cleaving peptide bonds of basic amino acids, leucine, or glycine in P1 position (nomenclature follows *Schechter & Berger [32])*. Papain exhibits a preference for an amino acid bearing a large hydrophobic side chain at the P2 position. It does not accept Val at the P1' position.

Limited and Extensive Proteolyses of Soybean Legumin

Glycinin, legumin from soybean (*Glycine max*) seeds, is composed of five kinds of subunits. On the basis of subunit primary structures, they are classified into two groups: type I (A1aB1b, A1bB2 and A2B1a) and type II (A3B4 and A5A4B3) [33].

During seed development, the single-chained subunit precursors are cleaved into α- and β-chains (N- and C-terminal domains, respectively) generating the mature two-chained glycinin subunits. These are assembled into the mature hexameric molecules composed of two trimers. In the mature subunit A5A4B3 (bad72975) a specific Asn residue, located in the central part of the α-chain *EF* loop (Figure 6), also is cleaved generating separate polypeptides A5 and A4. The 3D structures of proglycinin A1aB1b trimers 1FXZ [33] and glycinin A3B4 homo-hexamers 1OD5 [3] (Figure 1 and 7) are available.

Limited proteolysis of glycinin by trypsin [20] generates the detachment of α-chain C-terminal highly variable region HVR (the major part of the inter-domain linker) and point cleavages inside the α-chain *EF* loop and β-barrel/α-helix junction (Figure 6).

The β-chains were found to be uncleaved in glycinin-T, the final high-molecular-mass product of trypsinolysis, that has retained the primordial hexameric structure [24].

Proteolysis of glycinin by papain [14] is described below in more detail. According to SDS-PAGE data (Figure 8A) limited proteolysis of the intact glycinin (lane 1) by papain starts after as little as 6 min with the formation of several transient α-chain fragments, collectively denoted Ft (lane 2). SDS-PAGE of glycinin-P, the final product of the limited proteolysis, formed after 60 min, revealed a heterogeneous band F1 (21.9 kD in average) presumably derived from Ft by further proteolysis. In addition to the upper β-chain band, corresponding to the combination of similarly sized B1b, B2, B1a and B3 chains (from 20.3 kD to 20.7 kD) and the lower β-chain band B4 (19.3 kD), an intermediate-sized band denoted F2 (20.1 kD) is also seen. The α-chain A5 (10.6 kD) formed by the *in vivo* processing of α-chain A5A4 is also present. In addition, a 9.7 kD band F3 was detected.

All the enumerated bands were found in SDS-PAGE patterns of glycinin-P preparations before and after their purification by gel filtration from any low molecular mass products, suggesting that they remain associated together [14].

To follow the time course of glycinin-P formation, and to clarify the origin of the fragments F2 and F3, the relative molar amounts (and thus the relative number of particles) of the polypeptides detected by SDS-PAGE under reducing conditions were plotted vs. the reaction time (Figure 8B). Naturally, molar amounts of α-chains (excluding the α-chain A5) and β-chains are equal in the intact glycinin. After formation of glycinin-P, the sum of the molar amounts of β-chains present in glycinin-P are equal to those of β-chains in the intact glycinin.

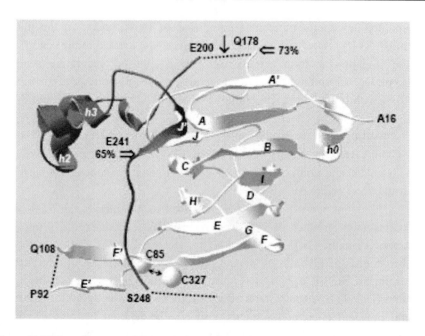

Figure 7. Ribbon diagram of the α-chain A3 from glycinin A3B4 structure 1OD5.
Additional strands E' and F' are specific of the chain A3. Three extended disordered
regions susceptible to limited proteolysis (a loop between Pro92 and Gln108; a β-
barrel/α-helix junction between Gln178 and Glu200; a hyper-variable region HVR
behind Ser248) are shown by dotted lines. Two spheres denote Cys residues that form
a disulfide bond between A3 (Cys85) and B4 (Cys327) α/β chains. Symbols $\Leftarrow$ and $\Rightarrow$
indicate Gln178 and Glu241 residues of highest accessibilities to the solvent in A3B4
structure (73 and 65%, respectively, as calculated with DeepView/Swiss-Pdb Viewer).
Dark part of the ribbon diagram corresponds to the sequence region detached during
formation of the final product of limited proteolysis, glycinin-P. An arrow indicates
position of Gly residue in central part of the disordered region between Gln178 and
Glu 200. This residue is conserved in all the five glycinin subunits.

Similarly, after formation of glycinin-P, the sum of the molar amounts of
the polypeptide fragments F1, F2 and F3 is equal to that of α-chains
(excluding the α-chain A5) present in the intact glycinin. These observations
indicate that 1) the β-chains are intact and thus inaccessible for limited
proteolysis during the formation of glycinin-P, and 2) that the fragments F1,
F2 and F3 are derived from α-chains. A slight decrease of the molar amounts
of the fragment F1 is observed, with the simultaneous increase in the molar
amounts of the fragment F2 observed before and shortly after formation of the
glycinin-P (Figure 8B). This suggests that a small part of the fragment F1 is

converted into the fragment F2. After this, the SDS-PAGE pattern of glycinin-P remains unchanged up to 24 h.

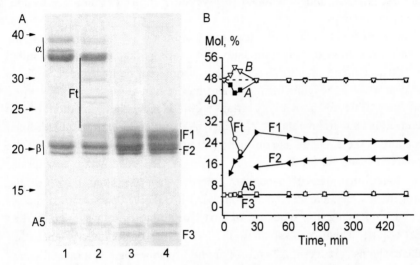

Figure 8. Time course of glycinin proteolysis by papain. A, SDS-PAGE in reducing conditions. Lane 1, intact glycinin; lane 2, intermediate products (6 min); lanes 3 and 4, glycinin-P (120 and 490 min, respectively). Numbers at the left side correspond to molecular masses (kD) of the markers. B, relative molar amounts of intermediate (Ft) and final polypeptides (F1, F2 and F3), and α-chain A5. The upper plots correspond to the sums of the molar amounts of β-chains (*B*) and α-chain fragments F1, F2 and F3 (*A*), respectively. The plots are expanded at the first stage of the reaction (0-60 min).

The relative molar amounts of the A5 chain and the fragment F3 are practically equal to each other, suggesting the origin of the latter from the A4 α-chain.

The apparent small increase of the summed molar amounts of the intact β-chains and the simultaneous equivalent decrease of the summed molar amounts of the α-chain fragments during the early stage of the reaction (up to 30 min, Figure 8B) suggest the transient formation of an additional α-chain fragment, Ft', which co-migrates with the upper band of the intact β-chains in SDS-PAGE.

Further analysis of the structure of glycinin-P by 2D SDS-PAGE (non-reducing and reducing conditions in the first and second dimensions, respectively) indicated that the α-chain fragments F1 and F2 are both covalently bound via disulfide bonds with intact type I and B4 β-chains [14].

The intact covalently bound pair A5/B3 (from glycinin A5A4B3) was also detected. The F3 band, which is resolved under the non-reducing conditions of the first dimension, probably corresponds to the product of limited proteolysis of the α-chain A4, and is retained in glycinin-P molecule due only to non-covalent interactions.

The above data allow the tentative prediction of the changes in the primary structures of glycinin subunits during the course of limited proteolysis. Among the three extended disordered regions susceptible to limited proteolysis (Figure 6), the C-terminal region HVR was shown to be most susceptible for proteolytic attack [20]. Hence, the formation of the several transient fragments Ft (Figure 8A) due to a gradual C-terminal truncation of the α-chains is confidently predicted. It seems unlikely that the fragments F1 and F2 are formed due to further cleavages within structurally stable N-terminal part of α-chains. Indeed, when the central part of the heterogeneous fragment F1 band from SDS-PAGE was subjected to the N-terminal sequencing, the sequence of first five amino acids was identified as LREQA- [14], which corresponds to the N-terminus of the intact α-chain A2. As the α-chains A1a, A1b, A2 and A3 are highly homologous, it indeed seems likely that the fragments F1 and F2 comprise the N-terminal portions of these four α-chains.

Assuming the apparent molecular masses (from SDS-PAGE data) of the fragments F1 and F2 approximate the true values, the cleavage sites of the four α chains can be approximated as well. These would fall within the susceptible β-barrel/α-helix junction (Figure 9). Therefore, it seems very probable that the final fragments F1/F2 detected by SDS-PAGE correspond to a 'denudate', but still structurally stable, β-barrel. Notably, the region of the β-barrel/α-helix junction in the A3B4 structure is N-terminally bordered by the Gln178 residue which is extremely accessible to the solvent (Figure 7). The enhanced accessibility to solvent of amino acid residues has been shown to coincide with an enhanced susceptibility to proteolytic attack [28].

Interestingly, the *EF* loop of the glycinin α-chains, which is susceptible to trypsin attack [20] (see above), exhibits a high resistance to the attack by papain.

In this context it should be noted that the proteolysis of the non-covalently bound α-chain A4 during papain attack might be specific. The A4 N-terminus, which covers almost the entire region of the disordered *EF* loop may be susceptible for limited proteolysis and detached during F3 formation.

```
-A'-A-B-C-D-E*---F-G-H-I-J----↓---helices-J'----HVR---

|--------21.5-21.6--------|---5.4-5.7---|-4.6-9.4-| AI & A3
   F1 21.9
   F2 20.1


|---10.6---||---11.0----|----5.6----|---13.6---| A5A4B3
 A5 10.6          F3 9.7
```

Figure 9. Schematic presentation of glycinin and glycinin-P α-chain structures. The α-chains from the group I subunits (AI), and A3, and in vivo processed A5A4 are shown. Numbers correspond to molecular masses (kD) of three polypeptide regions: β-barrel (A' through J strands), α-helices, and the extended disordered C-terminus HVR. Apparent molecular masses of the fragments F1, F2 and F3 as determined by SDS-PAGE are shown below in italics. An asterisk (*) following the E strand indicates position of a Cys residue involved in formation of the α-β inter-chain disulfide bridge. An arrow (↓) indicates the position of conserved Gly residue in central part of the disordered β-barrel/α-helix junction. The sequence region shown in bold corresponds to the structure of glycinin-P α-chains composed of a 'denudate' β-barrel [14].

Comparison of molecular mass values of glycinin-P determined experimentally by gel filtration (245 kD) and calculated from the number-average molecular mass of glycinin-P subunits (247 kD) indicated that glycinin-P maintains the primordial hexameric structure irrespective of the loss of α-chain helical region [14] as shown in Figure 7 and 9.

In the course of proteolysis, two stages of the reaction are evident when the relative weight concentrations of the residual protein P are plotted vs. the reaction time t (Figure 10A). In the first stage (up to 60 min of the reaction) the limited proteolysis, which generates the transient α-chain fragments Ft and subsequently the final fragments F1-F3, occurs. In the second stage the proteolysis proceeds as a pseudo-first order reaction that is indicative of the cleavage of the residual protein modified by limited proteolysis (glycinin-P) by the one-by-one mechanism (Table 1).

In the earliest stage of the reaction, the coincidence of the relative P and M values (Figure 10A) indicates that the onset of the one-by-one proteolysis is delayed. Therefore, the initial limited proteolysis might be a prerequisite for the onset of one-by-one proteolysis of glycinin. However, both plots 1 and 2 are highly curvilinear at the first stage suggesting possible reduced accuracy of the P and especially M values determined experimentally. In a second approximation, a more convincing conclusion can be made via comparison of linear parts of the plots 1 and 2.

As it was mentioned above, the values (100%-M%)+P% plotted vs. the reaction time t describes the kinetics of an exclusively one-by-one proteolysis (Figure 10A, plot 3). Extrapolation of the linear part of the plot 3 (60-1440 min) to zero time led to P value that exceeds 100%. The excess above 100% seems to be low (Figure 10B).

However, it should be taken into consideration that the slope of the linear part of the plot 3 is based upon 14 separate experimental values (P% and M% determinations during the reaction course). Therefore, after linearization of plot 3 the obtained value of the excess is accurate enough (0.76±0.06%). Hence, the fact of the excess is reliable and itself can be regarded as a strong qualitative indication that the rate constant of the one-by-one process depends on limited proteolysis.

It should be taken into consideration that the limited proteolysis deflects from ideality shown in Table 1. Hence, low but quickly increasing amounts of glycinin-P as a substrate for one-by-one proteolysis should appear before completion of the first stage of the reaction.

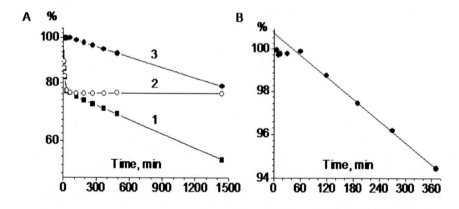

Figure 10. Kinetics of glycinin proteolysis. A, plot 1 (-■-), weight concentration P of the residual protein, and plot 2 (-○-), its molecular mass M. P and M are expressed as percentage of the initial values. Plot 3 (-●-), ([100%-M%]+P%) describes the kinetics of exclusive one-by-one proteolysis. B, plot 3, as in A, but enlarged initial portion of the reaction. The ordinate axis in both graphs is logarithmic.

In summary, the kinetics of limited and one-by-one proteolyses analyzed separately (Figure 10, plots 2 and 3, respectively) supports the model that limited proteolysis regulates (or even triggers) massive degradation of glycinin by the one-by-one mechanism.

This conclusion implies the gradual accumulation of structural alterations of the glycinin 3D structure during limited proteolysis, finalized by the formation of the glycinin-P of a constant structure that has acquired a consistently high susceptibility to unlimited degradation.

Three glycinin subunits form a trimer due to interactions with interfaces between the barrel domains, between the barrel and helix domains, and between the helix domains [33]. In the crystal structure 2D5H of glycinin A3B4, 23 hydrogen bonds were detected to be responsible for interactions between A and B subunits neighboring in the trimer. One half of these bonds disappear during glycinin-P formation due to removal of the α-chain C-terminal sequence region encompassing the helix domain and strand J', together with a short C-terminally adjacent structurally ordered segment (Figure 11).

In a similar way, one third of the hydrogen bonds responsible for interactions between A and B subunits of proglycinin 1FXZ trimer [33] should disappear during glycinin-P formation from mature A1aB1b homo-trimer. Notwithstanding the removal of the enumerated structural elements from the α-chains of glycinin-P, the latter retains the primordial hexameric structure. Loosened interactions between subunits might be the most plausible explanation for the acquisition of the enhanced susceptibility of glycinin-P to massive degradation via the one-by-one mechanism. However, a reorganization of the hexameric glycinin-P 3D structure generated by limited proteolysis can not be excluded.

The *in vivo* formation of Ft-like transient fragments followed by the gradual accumulation of F1-like 21.9-kD fragments of glycinin α-chains as the major product of *in vivo* limited proteolysis, as well as the relative stability of β-chains, were described long ago [34].

Hence, the general regularities of limited proteolysis *in vivo* catalyzed by endogenous papain-like proteinases [26, 27] and that described here *in vitro* with papain appear to be similar.

The degradation of β-chains *in vivo* is probably delayed due to the delayed onset of massive glycinin degradation via the one-by-one mechanism. Thus, limited proteolysis can be suggested to play the regulatory role in massive degradation of glycinin during seedling growth as well as *in vitro* as shown here.

The approach described above was used to the elucidation of the relationships between limited and one-by-one proteolyses in degradation of legumin and vicilin in other species.

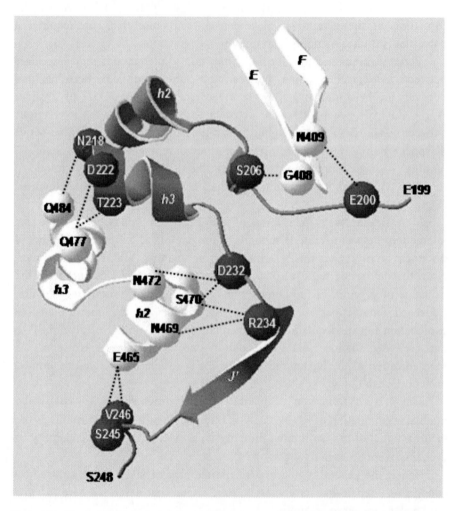

Figure 11. The hydrogen bonds (dotted lines) responsible for interactions between subunits A and B neighboring in the trimer of glycinin A3B4 structure 2D5H. The ribbon diagram is restricted to the C-terminal region of the α-chain A3 of the subunit A (dark part of the diagram) and two relevant regions of the β-chain B4 of the subunit B. Residues involved in formation of hydrogen bonds (distances 2.6-3.3 Å) are indicated as spheres.

Degradation of Oat 11S Globulin by Papain

The structure of cereal 11S globulin-like proteins is specific. According to Osborn's classification, they belong to glutelins, the alkali-soluble proteins. The oat 11S globulin (OG) soluble in salt solutions represents an exception [35] although its primary structure is closely similar to that of rice glutelin [36]. Thus, the OG can be regarded as an intermediate between legumins from eudicots and cereal glutelins.

In the course of OG proteolysis by papain, both the weight concentration P and molecular mass M of the residual protein decline quickly during the first 15 min of the reaction (Figure 12). After formation OG-P, the final product of limited proteolysis, the P value (plot 1) declines strongly under only negligible losses of the molecular mass M (plot 2). As was described above, the value of (100%-M%)+P% plotted vs. the reaction time t describes the kinetics of an exclusively one-by-one proteolysis (plot 3). Extrapolation of plot 3 to zero time leads to a P value close to 100%. This result suggests that the one-by-one proteolysis starts from the very beginning of the reaction, independent of the limited proteolysis that occurs in parallel.

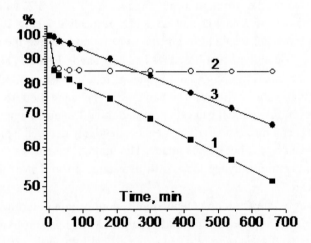

Figure 12. Kinetics of proteolysis of OG by papain. Plot 1 (-■-), weight concentration P of the residual protein, and plot 2 (-○-), its molecular mass M. P and M are expressed as percentage of the initial values. Plot 3 (-●-), (100%-M%)+P%, describes the kinetics of one-by-one proteolysis. The ordinate axis is logarithmic.

In summary, the OG degradation pattern represents an example of the independent occurrence of limited and one-by-one proteolysis. In this case, the functional role of extended hydrophilic sequence regions in OG primary structure is restricted to quick mobilization of the susceptible part of this protein reserve. The degradation pattern of soybean vicilin described below exemplifies this very case.

Limited and One-by-One Proteolysis of Soybean Vicilin

The trimer of β-conglycinin, the vicilin from soybean (*Glycine max*) seeds is formed due to chance combination of α, α' and β subunits. The α and α' (baa74452, see Figure 6) subunits are convicilin-like each containing a hydrophilic N-terminal extension. Closely similar 3D structures of β subunit trimers 1IPK [4] (Figure 13A) and of the core region of α' subunit trimers 1UIK [37] are available. The limited proteolysis of β-conglycinin *in* vivo and *in* vitro has been characterized (Figure 13B).

The hydrolysis of β-conglycinin β homotrimer (β$_3$-conglycinin) by papain [29] begins with the formation of fragments F1 and F2 with apparent molecular masses of 25.5 kD and 23.9 kD, respectively (Figure 14A). No bands of intermediate transient fragments were found between the upper band of the intact β$_3$-conglycinin (49.9 kD) and the bands F1/F2. Therefore, the cleavage of the intact β$_3$-conglycinin sequence into the two similarly sized N- and C-terminal subunit halves (domains) can be suggested to be a first proteolytic event. A gradual truncation of the initial fragments into a fragment F1a (25.1 kD) and three smaller fragments collectively denoted F2a (23.5-22.3 kD) is produced by further papain attack. The limited proteolysis is slow, with intact β$_3$-conglycinin polypeptide is still detectable up to 7 h of the reaction (Figure 14A).

Interestingly, the *EF* loop extended in β$_3$-conglycinin C-terminal domains is inaccessible to the attack by papain (Figure 14A) and papain-like proteinase CPPh [28] as well as *in vivo* [38] but it is cleaved by trypsin [20] generating the fragments F3t and F4t (Figure 14B).

In a similar way, structurally equivalent *EF* loop extended in glycinin α-chains is inaccessible to papain attack and *in vivo* [14] but it is cleaved by trypsin [20].

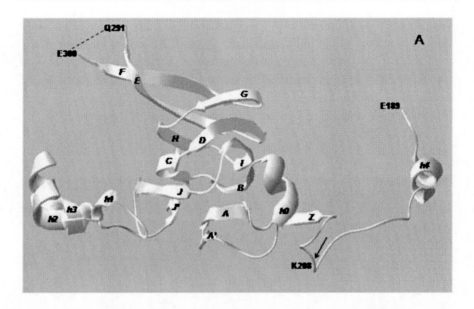

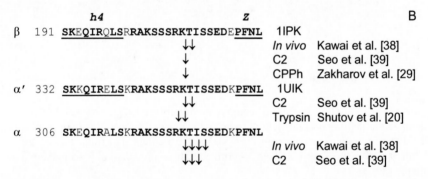

Figure 13. Susceptibility of β-conglycinin inter-domain linker to limited proteolysis. A, Ribbon diagram of β₃-conglycinin structure pdb|1IPK restricted to the C-terminal domain and the inter-domain linker. An arrow indicates position of the peptide bond K208-T209 most susceptible to the limited proteolysis. An extended disordered loop between β-strands E and F is shown by a dotted line (Q291-E300). B, The sequences of the inter-domain linker regions of β-conglycinin subunits exhibit an enhanced susceptibility to proteolytic attack. Arrows indicate cleavages identified from in vivo proteolysis and generated by the in vitro action of papain-like proteinases specific of germinating soybean (C2) and common bean (CPPh) seeds, and trypsin.

The described pattern of β₃-conglycinin proteolysis by papain is similar to that observed *in vivo* [38] and *in vitro* under the action of the endogenous papain-like soybean proteinase C2 [39] and the papain-like proteinase CPPh from germinating common beans [28] (Figure 13B). Therefore, it seems likely that the formation of the initial fragments F1 and F2 is due to cleavage of the bond K208-T209 that is also most susceptible to the action of C2, CPPh, and probably of trypsin (Figure 13B). This suggestion is supported by formation of the initial fragments F1t and F2t during β_3-conglycinin trypsinolysis (Figure 14B) which are identical in size to the fragments F1 and F2, respectively.

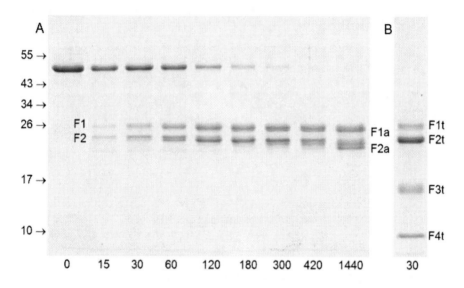

Figure 14. SDS-PAGE pattern of β_3-conglycinin hydrolysis. A, papain action; B, trypsin action. Numbers at the bottom indicate the reaction time in min. Numbers at the left side correspond to molecular masses (kD) of the markers. The fragments F1 and F2 correspond to the C-terminal and N-terminal halves (domains) of β_3-conglycinin subunits [29].

The protein weight concentration falls down quickly from the very start of the reaction, (Figure 15, plot 1). However, only a small part of the intact β_3-conglycinin is cleaved into subunit halves (Figure 14A). This observation immediately suggests that at least a portion of the intact β_3-conglycinin is susceptible to the one-by-one proteolysis.

The SDS-PAGE pattern during the course of proteolysis (Figure 14A), and the relative molecular mass (M%) of the residual protein plotted vs. the reaction time t (Figure 15, plot 2), indicates a slow limited proteolysis (the cleavage of the intact chains into the fragments F1/F2 followed by their slight truncation) occurs along the entire period analyzed. The relative weight concentration (P%) of the residual protein falls quickly at the first 2 h (the first step of the reaction) and decreases much slower thereafter in the second step (Figure 15, plot 1). A large difference in the rates of the extensive proteolysis during the first rapid and the second slower steps of the reaction suggests the existence of two forms of the intact β_3-conglycinin, A and B, differing in their susceptibility to papain attack. After exhaustion of the most susceptible form A in the first step, the plot 3 describes the kinetics of the exclusively one-by-one proteolysis of the less susceptible form B.

The rate constant of the one-by-one proteolysis of the form B is changeless after two hours of the reaction (Figure 15).

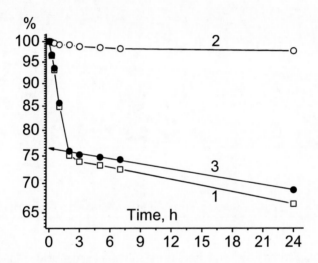

Figure 15. Kinetics of proteolysis of β_3-conglycinin by papain. Plot 1 (-□-), weight concentration P of the residual protein, and plot 2 (-○-), its molecular mass M. P and M are expressed as percentage of the initial values. Plot 3 (-●-), (100%-M%)+P%, describes the kinetics of extensive proteolysis. An arrow indicates extrapolation of the linear part of the plot 3 to zero time. The ordinate axis is logarithmic.

This is independent of the intact β_3-conglycinin subunits still present in the reaction mixture (up to 5 h, Figure 14A), and the truncation of subunit halves that continued up to 24 h. These observations support the above suggestion that the limited and one-by-one proteolyses of the form B occur independently, in parallel, in both the first and the second stages of the reaction. The extrapolation of the linear part of the plot 3 to zero time should lead to the P% value equal to the percentage of the form B in the initial β_3-conglycinin preparation (i.e., 76%).

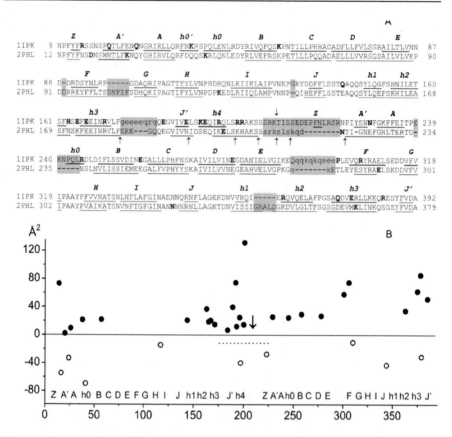

Figure 16. Comparison of accessibilities to the solvent of amino acid residues in chains of β₃-conglycinin (1IPK) and phaseolin (2PHL). Accessible surface area (ASA) of amino acid residues in the protein structures was estimated with the program NACCESS, which implements the algorithm of Lee and Richards [42]. A, Structural alignment of 1IPK and 2PHL sequences. Lower case letters indicate disordered regions. Positions that cannot be used for 1IPK and 2PHL comparison are shaded in grey. Bold letters indicate residues of ASA >110 Å² in 1IPK and 2PHL sequences. Arrows denote point cleavage of β₃-conglycinin that generates the fragments F1/F1t and F2/F2t (↓) and cleavages of phaseolin by concerted action of endogenous papain-like proteinase CPPh and Asn-specific legumain LLP (↑). B, Comparison of ASA values exceeding 110 Å² in 1IPK and 2PHL structures. Residue numbering (abscissa) correspond to β₃-conglycinin sequence aligned with that of phaseolin. In respective matching alignment positions, ASA values of 2PHL residues were subtracted from those of 1IPK. The resulting positive and negative values are shown by closed and open circles, respectively. An arrow (↓) denotes the position of the point cleavage of β₃-conglycinin by papain and trypsin. A dotted line indicates the region of phaseolin sequence detached by limited proteolysis catalyzed by concerted action of CPPh and LLP.

The question remains as to whether the form A of β_3-conglycinin that is highly susceptible to extensive proteolysis exists *in vivo*, or if it results due to partial denaturation of the protein preparations during isolation procedures. In this context, it should be noted that different isomeric β-conglycinin β subunit exist in dry soybean seeds [40] and that the value of the rate constant of the one-by-one proteolysis is highly sensitive to the conformational state of a protein substrate [41].

The susceptibility to the one-by-one proteolysis seems to be an intrinsic feature of the native β_3-conglycinin structure as observed in the kinetics above (Figure 15). In contrast, the similarly organized 3D structure of the highly homologous [4] phaseolin (2PHL), is inaccessible to one-by-one proteolysis under the action of the endogenous papain-like proteinase CPPh and other enzymes, including papain (see above). Conversion of phaseolin into a form susceptible to one-by-one proteolysis requires the concerted action of two endogenous enzymes, the papain-like proteinase CPPh and an Asn-specific legumain LLP (Figure 16) [28, 29]. Hence, the stability to proteolysis of phaseolin, as well as the susceptibility of β_3-conglycinin, reflect differences in the inherent structural features of these native storage globulins.

The enhanced accessibility to the solvent of an amino acid residue in a protein structure has been shown to coincide with an enhanced susceptibility to proteolytic attack [28]. This relationship was used here for comparison of the fine structural differences between β_3-conglycinin and phaseolin expected to be relevant to their different susceptibilities to one-by-one proteolysis. The number of residues of enhanced accessible surface areas ASA (>110 $\mathring{A}^2$) was found to be different in β_3-conglycinin and phaseolin structures (27 compared to 9 residues, respectively, Figure 16). This difference reflects the specifically low packing density in β_3-conglycinin molecules responsible for their high susceptibility to the one-by-one proteolysis.

CONCLUSION

The evolutionary pathway leading to the present day seed storage globulins vicilin and legumin can be thought to have occurred in two stages. In the first, the β-barrel/α-helix motif preexisting as a core of the bacterial oxalate decarboxylase structures was chosen as a suitable stable basis for a storage form. An early step in this direction is reflected in the hypothetical storage globulin-like proteins from the club moss *S. moellendorfii* and in a vicilin-like protein synthesized in the developing spores of the fern *M. struthiopteris* [6,7]. The similarity in expression regulatory mechanisms of the fern spore protein gene and of the genes of seed storage globulins [8] supports the idea that the storage globulin-like proteins from non-seed plants serve as primitive storage proteins.

However, this primitive storage protein structure was apparently too stable, and not suitable for the demands of a rapid mobilization via proteolysis needed during early seed germination and subsequent early seedling growth. As a consequence, the second stage of storage protein evolution was marked by the insertion of hydrophilic extensions within the primitive storage protein structure. These extensions, while maintaining the basic β-barrel/α-helix and its stability, introduced the possibility of the controlled proteolysis of these proteins. Such extensions, usually lacking defined secondary structure, became the sites for the initiating proteolytic attack. Indeed, in the present day vicilin- and legumin-type proteins these are cleaved during the early stages of seedling growth, providing a quick albeit limited mobilization of this now susceptible part of the seed protein reserves. These initial cleavages follow the limited proteolysis mechanism, as opposed to the subsequent massive degradation that occurs subsequently by the one-by-one mechanism.

The exact pathway of degradation has been found to differ with different storage globulins in different plant species. When the packing density of storage globulin molecules is relatively low, their degradation follows a mixed-type mechanism, i.e. the limited proteolysis of the susceptible sites and the unlimited degradation of the entire molecule by the one-by-one mechanism occur in parallel from the very beginning of the reaction. The degradation patterns of soybean β-conglycinin β homotrimer and, most likely, the oat legumin-like 11S globulin, exemplify this case.

In other cases, the native protein substrate is inaccessible to deep degradation by the one-by-one mechanism due to a relatively high packing density of its molecules. This is represented by the degradation of phaseolin, the vicilin from common beans, and glycinin, the legumin from soybeans. Therefore, the onset of the one-by-one degradation both of phaseolin and glycinin molecules is delayed until the completion of the limited proteolysis. Thus, a structural alteration of these proteins generated by limited proteolysis triggers their subsequent massive degradation by the one-by-one mechanism.

The origin and successive development of the structure of storage globulins have been described in this chapter in the context of their functional specificity during seed development followed by seed storage and subsequent germination and seedling growth.

REFERENCES

[1] Casey, R. (1999) Distribution and some properties of seed globulins. In P. R. Shewry & R. Casey (Eds.), Seed Proteins (pp. 159-169) Dordrecht, The Netherlands: Kluwer Academic Publishers.

[2] Shutov, A. D., Blattner, F. R., Bäumlein, H. & Müntz, K. (2003) Storage and mobilization as antagonistic functional constraints of seed storage globulin evolution. *J. Exp. Bot.* 54, 1645-1654.

[3] Adachi, M., Kanamori, J., Masuda T., Yagasaki, K., Kitamura, K., Mikami, B. & Ursumi, S. (2003) Crystal structure of soybean 11S globulin: glycinin A3B4 homohexamer. *Proc. Natl. Acad. Sci. USA* 100, 7395-7400.

[4] Maruyama, N., Adachi, M., Takahashi, K., Yagasaki, A., Kohno, M., Takenaka, Y., Okuda, E., Nakagawa, S., Mikami, B. & Utsumi, S. (2001) Crystal structures of recombinant and native soybean β-conglycinin β homotrimers. *Eur. J. Biochem.* 268, 3595-3604.

[5] Dunwell, J. M., Culham, A., Carter, C. E., Sosa-Aguirre, C. R. & Goodenpugh, P. W. (2001) Evolution of functional diversity in the cupin superfamily. *Trends Biochem. Sci.* 26, 740-746.

[6] Shutov, A. D., Braun H., Chesnokov, Yu. V. & Bäumlein, H. (1998) A gene encoding a vicilin-like protein is specifically expressed in fern spores. Evolutionary pathway of seed storage globulins. *Eur. J. Biochem.* 252, 79-89.

[7] Kakhovskaya, I. A., Rudakova, A. S. & Manteuffel, R. (2003) Legumin-like and vicilin-like proteins from spores of the fern Matteuccia struthiopteris. *J. Plant Physiol.* 160, 583-588.

[8] Schallau, A., Kakhovskaya, I., Tewes, A., Czihal, A., Tiedemann, J., Mohr, M., Grosse, I., Manteuffel, R. & Bäumlein, H. (2008) Phylogenetic footprints in fern spore- and seed-specific gene promoters. *Plant J.* 53, 414-424.

[9] Shutov, A. D. & Kakhovskaya, I. A. (2011) Evolution of seed storage globulins and cupin superfamily. *Mol. Biol.* (Moscow) 45, 529-535.

[10] Woo, E. J., Dunwell, J. M., Goodenough, P. W., Marvier, A. C. & Pikersgill, R. W. (2000). Germin is a manganese containing homohexamer with oxalate oxidase and superoxide dismutase activities. *Nature Struct. Biol.* 7, 1036-1040.

[11] Dunwell, J. M. & Gane, P. J. (1998) Microbial relatives of seed storage proteins; conservation of motifs in a functionally diverse superfamily of enzymes. *J. Mol. Evol.* 46, 147-154.

[12] Bäumlein, H., Braun, H., Kakhovskaya, I. A. & Shutov, A.D. (1995) Seed storage proteins of spermatophytes share a common ancestor with desiccation proteins of fungi. *J. Mol. Evol.* 41, 1070-1075.

[13] Van de Peer, Y. & De Wachter, R. (1994) TREECON for Windows: a software package for the construction and drawing of evolutionary trees for the Microsoft Windows environment. Comput. *Appl. Biosci.* 10, 569-570.

[14] Shutov, A., Rudakova, A., Rudakov, S., Kakhovskaya, I., Schallau, A., Maruyama, N. & Wilson, K. (2012) Limited proteolysis regulates massive degradation of glycinin, storage 11S globulin from soybean seeds: An in vitro model. *J. Plant Physiol.* 169, 1227-1233.

[15] Martin, W., Rujan, T., Richly, E., Hansen, A., Cornelsen, S., Lins, T., Leister, D., Stoebe, B., Hasegawa, M. & Penny, D. (2002) Evolutionary analysis of Arabidopsis, cyanobacterial, and chloroplast genomes reveals plastid phylogeny and thousands of cyanobacterial genes in the nucleus. *Proc. Natl. Acad. Sci. USA* 99, 12246-12251.

[16] Qiu, H., Price, D. C., Weber, A. P. M., Facchinelli, F., Yoon, H. S. & Bhattacharya, D. (2013) Assessing the bacterial contribution to the plastid proteome. *Trends Plant Sci.* 18, 680-687.

[17] Shutov, A. D., Kakhovskaya, I. A., Braun, H., Bäumlein, H. & Müntz K. (1995) Legumin and vicilin-like seed storage proteins: evidence for a common single-domain ancestral gene. *J. Mol. Evol.* 41, 1057-1069.

[18] Shutov, A. D., Braun, H., Chesnokov, Yu. V., Horstmann, C., Kakhovskaya, I. A. & Bäumlein, H (1998) Sequence peculiarity of gnetalean legumin-like seed storage proteins. *J. Mol. Evol.* 47, 486-492.

[19] Häger, K. P., Müller, B., Wind., C., Erbach, S. & Fischer H. (1996) Evolution of legumin genes: loss of an ancestral intron at the beginning of angiosperm diversification. *FEBS Lett.* 387, 94-98.

[20] Shutov, A. D., Kakhovskaya, I. A., Bastrygina, A. S., Bulmaga, V. P., Horstmann, C., & Müntz, K. (1996) Limited proteolysis of β-conglycinin and glycinin, the 7S and 11S storage globulins from soybean (Glycine max (L.) Merr.): structural and evolutionary implications. *Eur. J. Biochem.* 241, 221-228.

[21] Tandang-Silvas, M. R. G., Fukuda, T., Fukuda, C., Prak, K., Cabanos, C., Kimura, A., Itoh, T., Mikami, B., Utsumi, S. & Maruyama, N. (2010)

Conservation and divergence on plant seed 11S globulins based on crystal structures. *Biochim. Biophys. Acta* 1804, 1432–1442.

[22] Lane, B. G. (1994) Oxalate, germin and the extracellular matrix. *FASEB Journal* 8, 294-301.

[23] Rupley, J. A. (1967) Susceptibility to attack by proteolytic enzymes. *Methods Enzymol.* 11, 905-17.

[24] Shutov, A. D., Pineda, J., Senyuk, V. I., Reva, V. A. & Vaintraub, I. A. (1991) Action of trypsin on soybean glycinin. Mixed-type proteolysis and its kinetics; molecular mass of glycinin-T. *Eur. J. Biochem.* 199, 539-543.

[25] Vaintraub, I. A. (1998) Kinetics of co-operative proteolysis. *Nahrung* 42, 59-60.

[26] Shutov, A.D. & Vaintraub, I.A. (1987) Degradation of storage proteins in germinating seeds. *Phytochemistry* 26, 1557-1566.

[27] Tan-Wilson, A. L. & Wilson, K. A. (2012) Mobilization of seed protein reserves. *Physiol. Plant.* 145, 140-153.

[28] Zakharov, A., Carchilan, M., Stepurina, T., Rotari, V., Wilson, K. & Vaintraub, I. (2004) Comparative study of the role of the major proteinases of germinated common bean (Phaseolus vulgaris L.) and soybean (Glycine max (L.) Merrill) seeds in the degradation of their storage proteins. *J. Exp. Bot.* 55, 2241-2249.

[29] Shutov, A. D., Rudakova, A. S., Rudakov, S. V., Kakhovskaya, I. A., Schallau, A. A., Wilson, K. A. & Maruyama, N. (2013) Degradation of β-conglycinin β-homotrimer by papain: independent occurrence of limited and extensive proteolyses. *Bisci. Biotechnol. Biochem.* 77, 2082-2086.

[30] Rotari, V. I., Senyuk, V. I., Jivotovskaya, A. V., Horstmann, C. & Vaintraub, I. A. (1997) Proteinase A-like enzyme from germinated kidney bean seeds. Its action on phaseolin and vicilin. *Physiol. Plant.* 100, 171-177.

[31] Senyuk, V., Rotari, V., Becker, C., Zakharov, A., Horstmann, C., Müntz, K. & Vaintraub, I. 1998. Does an asparaginyl-specific cysteine endopeptidase trigger phaseolin degradation in cotyledons of kidney bean? *Eur. J. Biochem.* 258, 546-558.

[32] Schechter, I. & Berger, A. (1967) On the size of the active site in proteases. I. Papain. Biochem. *Biophys. Res. Commun.* 27, 157-162.

[33] Adachi, M., Takenaka, Y., Gidamis, A. B., Mikami, B. & Utsumi, S. (2001). Crystal structure of soybean proglycinin A1aB1b homotrimer. *J. Mol. Biol.* 305, 291-305.

[34] Wilson, K. A., Rightmire, B. R., Chen, J. C., Tan-Wilson, A. L. (1986) Differential proteolysis of glycinin and β-conglycinin polypeptides during soybean germination and seedling growth. *Plant Physiol.* 82, 71-76.

[35] Klose, C. & Arendt, E. K. (2012) Proteins in oats; their synthesis and changes during germination: a review. *Crit. Rev. Food Sci. Nutr.* 52, 629-639.

[36] Shotwell, M. A., Afonso, C., Davies, E., Chesnut, R. S. & Larkins, B. A. (1988) Molecular characterization of oat seed globulins. *Plant Physiol.* 87, 698-704.

[37] Maruyama, Y., Maruyama, N., Mikami, B. & Utsumin, S. (2003) Structure of the core region of the soybean β-conglycinin α' subunit. *Acta Cryst.* D60, 289-297.

[38] Kawai, M, Susuki, S, Asano, M., Miwa, T. & Shibai, H. (1997) Characterization of 30-kDa fragments derived from beta-conglycinin degradation process during germination and seedling growth of soybean. *Biosci. Biothech. Biochem.* 61, 794-799.

[39] Seo, S., Tan-Wilson, A. & Wilson, K.A. (2001) Protease C2, a cysteine endopeptidase involved in the continuing mobilization of soybean β-conglycinin seed proteins. *Biochim. Biophys.* Acta, 1545, 192-206.

[40] Ladin, B. F., Tierney, M. L., Meinke, D. W., Hosángadi, P., Veith, M. & Beachy, R.N. (1987) Developmental regulation of beta-conglycinin in soybean axes and cotyledons. *Plant Physiol.* 84, 35-41.

[41] Vaintraub, I. A. & Morari, D. (2003) Applying the increase in rate constants of cooperative proteolysis to the determination of transition curves of protein denaturation. *J. Biochem. Biophys. Methods* 57:191-201.

[42] Lee, B. & Richards, F. M. (1971) The interpretation of protein structures: estimation of static accessibility. *J. Mol. Biol.* 55, 379-400.

INDEX

#

21st century, 43

A

Abraham, 26
access, 55
accessibility, 88, 99, 104
acetylation, 64
acid, vii, 2, 9, 44, 46, 58, 59, 60, 84, 98
active site, 103
acute glaucoma, 36
additives, 60
adenosine, 35
adhesion, 15, 16, 25, 51
adipose tissue, 25
African Americans, 9
age, 9, 11, 17, 19, 20
aggregation, 67
agriculture, 63
albumin, 12, 17, 44, 58, 64
algae, 77
algorithm, 98
allergens, 36, 38
allergic reaction, ix, 29, 32, 34, 47
allergy, 36, 38, 51
alpha1-antitrypsin, 12
amaranth globulins, vii, 51
Amaranth proteins, ix, 41, 51, 69

amino acid(s), ix, 13, 41, 42, 43, 44, 45, 46,
    48, 54, 58, 60, 77, 78, 84, 88, 98, 99
amylase, 50
amyloid deposits, 18, 25
amyloidosis, viii, 2, 9, 16, 17, 18, 19, 25, 26
anaphylactic reactions, 36
anaphylactic shock, ix, 30, 35, 38
anaphylaxis, vii, ix, 29, 34, 36, 38, 39, 51,
    64
ancestors, 77, 80
anemia, 13, 18
angioedema, 35
angiosperm, 79, 102
angiotensin converting enzyme, 59
angiotensin II, 53
antibody(ies), vii, 1, 3, 4, 5, 6, 13, 15, 16,
    19, 22, 23, 25, 30, 31, 32, 33, 35, 38, 39,
    51
antigen, viii, 3, 5, 6, 7, 8, 15, 19, 21, 22, 29,
    30, 32, 34, 52, 62, 63, 70
antigen-presenting cell, 62
antihistamines, 35
antihypertensive agents, ix, 42
antioxidant, 57, 58, 63, 69
antitoxin, 30
antitumor, 60
apoptosis, 15, 51
aqueous solutions, 44
arteriosclerosis, 53, 54
aseptic, 34
aspartic acid, 51

assessment, 24, 26, 44, 68
asymptomatic, 9, 24
atoms, 73
attachment, 36
autonomic neuropathy, 17
autosomal recessive, 22

B

Bacillus subtilis, 77
bacteria, 48, 77
bacterium, 30
base pair, 7, 8
basophils, ix, 6, 30, 34, 35, 36, 37, 38, 39
benefits, 54, 55, 56, 58
benign, vii, 2, 3, 17
bile, 59
bile acids, 58
binding globulin, 12
bioavailability, 48
biochemical characteristics, vii
biochemistry, 74
bioinformatics, 45
biological activity, 63
biological systems, 57
biomarkers, 14, 21, 26
biomolecules, 57
biopsy, 20
biosynthesis, 68
biotechnology, 46
birefringence, 18
bleeding, 17
blood, ix, 3, 30, 36, 38, 53, 54, 55, 56, 58,
    59, 65, 68
blood flow, 38
blood pressure, 53, 54, 57, 59, 68
bloodstream, 12
bonds, x, 5, 49, 50, 72, 84, 87, 91, 92
bone marrow, vii, 2, 4, 9, 10, 13, 15, 16, 17,
    18, 24, 25
bone marrow biopsy, 18
bounds, 44
bradykinin, 53
brain, 59
breakdown, 50

breast milk, 34
bronchial asthma, 35
by-products, 49

C

calcium, 13, 17
cancer, 23, 24, 25, 51, 57, 63
capillary, viii, 2, 35
carbohydrate, 6, 36, 37, 38, 39
carboxyl, 55
carcinogenesis, 3, 21
cardiac involvement, 17
cardiomyopathy, 17
cardiovascular disease, 52, 57, 62
cardiovascular risk, 56
carotenoids, 57
carpal tunnel syndrome, 17
carrier globulins, vii, viii, 29, 30
Caucasians, 9
cDNA, 46, 60
cell biology, 22
cell culture, 55, 62
cell line, 11
cell membranes, 35
cell signaling, 3
cell surface, 15
cereal grains, ix, 42
ceruloplasmin, 12
cheese, 61
chemical, 47, 48, 50
chemotherapeutic agent, 16
chemotherapy, 26
childhood, 34
chloroplast, 102
cholesterol, 58, 59, 60, 66
chromatography, 47
chromosome, 31
chronic diseases, 51
chronic lymphocytic leukemia, 27
chymotrypsin, 83
circulation, ix, 10, 30, 35, 38
classes, ix, 7, 29, 32, 44
classification, 38, 43, 93

cleavage(s), x, 7, 72, 80, 82, 83, 84, 85, 88, 89, 94, 95, 96, 98, 100
clinical presentation, 20
clinical trials, 15, 26
clone, vii, 2, 3, 13
cloning, 60
coding, 7, 46
coffee, 36
colon cancer, 70
combination therapy, 16
commercial, 50, 63
complement, ix, 12, 30, 42
composition, 30, 43, 44, 46, 50, 60, 61, 69
compounds, 42, 54, 55, 56, 57, 58
Congo, 18
conjunctivitis, 35
consensus, 14, 19, 26
conservation, 102
construction, 102
consumption, ix, 41, 51, 56, 58
contamination, 55
cooking, 50, 61
cooling, 9
copper, 42
coronary heart disease, 52, 58
corticosteroids, 35
cost, 48, 55
cough, 53
covalent bond, 49
covering, 75
creatinine, 13
crop(s), 42, 43, 45, 46, 60, 64, 69
CRP, 12
crude oil, 60
cryopreservation, 66
crystal structure, 91, 103
CT, 38
cultivation, 43, 61, 69
cysteine, viii, 29, 31, 44, 103, 104
cytokines, 35, 52, 62
cytosine, 8
cytotoxicity, 6, 15, 25

D

deaths, 9, 34
defense mechanisms, 57
deficiencies, 22, 44
deficiency, 12, 22, 44
deficit, 42
degradation, x, 12, 17, 23, 72, 74, 82, 83, 84, 91, 92, 94, 100, 102, 103
degradation process, 104
dehydration, 12
denaturation, 44, 61, 99, 104
deposition, viii, 2, 16, 17, 19, 20, 27, 46
deposits, 19
desiccation, 102
destruction, 38
detachment, 85
detectable, 51, 77, 79, 94
detection, viii, 2, 13, 27
diabetes, 54
diagnostic criteria, 10
dialysis, 17
diarrhea, 17
diastolic blood pressure, 52
diet, 48, 51, 52
dietary fiber, 42, 43
digestibility, 59, 67, 68
digestion, 46, 54, 56, 58, 67
dipeptides, 55
discrimination, 21
disease progression, 14, 16
diseases, 3, 16, 17, 19, 20, 21, 26, 52, 54, 57
disorder, 13, 14, 17, 54
distributive shock, 35
diuretic, 36
divergence, 103
diversification, ix, 5, 9, 23, 38, 71, 78, 102
diversity, 3, 4, 6, 8, 20, 22, 101
DNA, 8, 22
DNA repair, 7
domain structure, x, 72, 73, 74, 79
domestication, 43
dough, 50, 63, 67
drawing, 102
drugs, 36, 53

dyscrasia, 9, 19

E

egg, 66
electron microscopy, 18, 25, 39
electrophoresis, viii, 2, 10, 12, 13, 14, 18, 24
elucidation, 92
encoding, 7, 45, 46, 60, 101
endosperm, 46, 68, 69
end-stage renal disease, 20, 52
energy, 16
engineering, 46
environment, 102
environmental conditions, 48, 60, 61
enzyme(s), 22, 45, 53, 55, 56, 57, 61, 62, 64, 65, 66, 67, 82, 69, 83, 84, 99, 102, 103
eosinophilia, 39
eosinophils, 34, 35
epidemic, 52
epithelial cells, 51
epitopes, 6, 38
erythrocytes, 38
ESRD, 20
eukaryotic, 77
evidence, ix, 18, 30, 77, 102
evolution, 22, 77, 79, 80, 82, 100, 101
excision, 8
excretion, vii, 1, 59
exons, 7
exposure, 8, 35
extracellular matrix, 16, 103
extracts, 52, 56, 66, 69
extrusion, 50, 62

F

fat, 18, 25, 50, 59
fatty acids, 43
fermentation, 56, 60
filtration, 85, 89
financial support, 59

first dimension, 88
flank, 7
flavonoids, 60
flavonol, 59
flexibility, 6, 32
flour, 42, 44, 50, 61, 64, 65
fluid, 10, 35
foams, 49
food, ix, 36, 41, 42, 43, 46, 48, 50, 51, 52, 54, 55, 56, 57, 60, 62, 63, 64, 66, 69
food industry, ix, 41, 48
food production, 60, 63
food products, 50, 51
food security, 42
foreign macromolecule, vii, viii, 29, 30
formation, 8, 48, 53, 58, 64, 74, 79, 84, 85, 86, 87, 88, 89, 91, 92, 93, 94, 96
fractures, 13
fragments, 6, 19, 84, 85, 86, 87, 88, 89, 91, 94, 96, 98, 104
free radicals, 57, 58
freezing, 49
fructose, 36
fruits, 36
functional changes, 62
functional food, 54, 55, 56, 58, 68
fungi, 74, 102

G

GABA, 59
gel, viii, 2, 24, 49, 50, 85, 89
gelation, 49, 62
gene promoter, 101
gene transfer, 77
genes, 5, 6, 7, 8, 18, 21, 45, 46, 77, 79, 80, 100, 102
genetic background, 47
genetic engineering, 46, 65
genome, 46, 77
genomics, 45, 70
genotype, 46
genus, 43
germination, x, 72, 79, 82, 100, 104
ginseng, 36

glycans, 36
glycine, 84
glycoprotein, vii, viii, 15, 16, 29, 30, 44
glycoproteins, vii, 1, 6, 36
goiter, 17
granules, 35
green alga, ix, 71, 74, 76, 77, 79
Green Revolution, 42
growth, x, 43, 66, 72, 82, 91, 100, 104
growth hormone, 55
guanine, 8
guardian, 31
guidelines, 20, 26, 27

H

hairy cell leukemia, 27
haptoglobin, 13
harbors, 47
hardness, 49, 50
health, 45, 54, 63
hematuria, 20
hemoglobin, 13
hemolytic anemia, 18
hepatomegaly, 17, 18
heterogeneity, 20, 21
histamine, 35
histone, 63, 64
history, 64
hormone, 12
host, vii, 1, 47, 77
human, ix, 5, 12, 15, 25, 27, 30, 31, 38, 41,
    48, 53, 54, 57, 62, 65, 70
human body, 57
human milk, 62
human subjects, 54
humoral immunity, 3, 15, 16, 20, 30
hydrogen, 49, 91, 92
hydrogen bonds, 91, 92
hydrogenation, 36
hydrolysis, 49, 56, 58, 66, 67, 83, 94, 96
hydrophobicity, 46, 47
hygiene, 34
hypercalcemia, 13
hypersensitivity, 34, 35, 51

hypertension, 20, 36, 53, 54, 55, 56, 68
hypotensive, 54, 57
hypotensive drugs, 53
hypothesis, 34

I

identification, viii, 2, 66
IFN, 52, 63
immune response, 5, 22, 33, 39, 52
immune system, 6, 15, 22, 35
immunity, 3, 20
immunofixation, viii, 2
immunogen, vii, 1
immunoglobulin(s), vii, viii, ix, 2, 6, 8, 9,
    10, 17, 19, 22, 23, 24, 26, 27, 29, 30, 31,
    32, 33, 38
immunoglobulin genes, 38
immunologically homogeneous proteins,
    vii, 2, 3
immunosuppression, 21
immunotherapy, viii, 2, 16, 25
improvements, 46
in vitro, ix, x, 15, 42, 47, 53, 54, 55, 56, 62,
    63, 64, 66, 67, 68, 72, 76, 82, 83, 91, 94,
    95, 102
in vivo, x, 54, 55, 56, 62, 63, 72, 76, 82, 83,
    84, 85, 89, 91, 94, 95, 99
incidence, 17, 23, 34
India, 42, 64
individual action, 83
individuals, 9
induction, 7
industry, 48, 59
infants, 34
inflammation, 12, 17
inflammatory cells, 35
influenza virus, 22
ingestion, 35
ingredients, 46, 48, 58, 60
inheritance, 77
inhibition, 53, 56, 57, 65
inhibitor, 55
initiation, 14, 19, 22
inoculation, 35

insertion, x, 55, 72, 79, 100
insulin, 54
integration, 46
intervention, 24
intracellular calcium, 34, 35
intron(s), 78, 79, 80, 102
isolation, 56, 99
Italy, 29

K

kidney, 17, 19, 20, 103
kill, 15
kinetics, x, 72, 84, 90, 91, 93, 97, 99, 103

L

Latin America, 42
LDL, 58, 59
lead, ix, 5, 19, 30, 34, 42, 97
legume, 44
lesions, 13, 54
leucine, 84
leukemia, 27
light, viii, 2, 3, 5, 9, 10, 13, 17, 18, 19, 20,
    21, 24, 25, 26, 27, 29, 31, 32, 33
lipid metabolism, 63
lipid oxidation, 67
lipids, 43
Lithuania, 61, 69
liver, vii, viii, 4, 12, 17, 20, 27, 29, 30, 36,
    59
liver disease, 12, 59
liver failure, 27
liver transplant, 36
liver transplantation, 36
livestock, 74
localization, 64
loci, 3, 20, 21, 27, 31
locus, 4, 5, 8
low risk, 55
lymph, 18
lymphadenopathy, 18
lymphatic tissues, vii, viii, 29, 30

lymphocytes, 3, 4, 8, 22, 30, 34, 52, 62, 64
lymphoid, 9, 21
lymphoma, 16, 19
lysine, 44

M

mAb, 15
macronutrients, 51
macrophages, 34, 35
magnesium, 42
major histocompatibility complex, 30
majority, 10, 18, 21, 43
malignancy, 9, 18, 21
malignant cells, 19, 21
mammalian cells, 46, 64
management, 26
manganese, 42, 101
manipulation, 47
mannitol, 36, 37, 39
marketing, 56
mass, 53, 82, 84, 85, 89, 93
mass media, 53
mass spectrometry, 84
mast cells, ix, 6, 30, 34, 35, 37, 38, 39
matrix, 49, 69
matter, 49
MBP, 35
mean arterial pressure, 55
measurement(s), 14, 26
media, 36
median, 17, 19, 20
medical, 35, 51
medication, 54
medicine, 23
memory, 5
memory B cells, 5
metabolic pathways, 57
metabolism, 59
MGUS, vii, 2, 3, 9, 13, 14, 16, 17, 19, 23,
    24
MHC, 30
mice, 20, 22, 47
Microsoft, 102
microstructure, 49

migration, vii, 1, 19
mild hypertensive, 64
mitochondrial DNA, 69
mixing, 50
models, 15, 54
modifications, 9, 50, 55, 61
molasses, 60, 67
Moldova, 71
molecular biology, 46, 74
molecular mass, 47, 82, 83, 84, 85, 87, 88, 89, 90, 93, 94, 96, 97, 103
molecular weight, 16, 45
molecules, x, 3, 6, 58, 72, 74, 82, 85, 99, 100
monoclonal antibody, 15, 25
monoclonal gammopathies, vii, viii, 2, 3, 9, 10, 12, 14, 17, 20, 21, 24, 27
monoclonal protein, vii, viii, 2, 13, 24
Moscow, 101
motif, 8, 74, 99
M-protein, vii, 2, 3, 10, 14
MR, 24
mucosa, 6
multiple myeloma, vii, viii, 2, 9, 19, 23, 24, 25, 27, 28, 31
multivariate analysis, 14
muscles, 57
mutation(s), 8, 21, 27, 69

N

NaCl, 61
National Health and Nutrition Examination Survey, 63
necrosis, 51
negative consequences, 57
nephrotic syndrome, 12, 17
nervous system, 20
Netherlands, 101
neutral, 44
neutrophils, 34, 35
nitrogen, 45, 57
NK cells, 6
Nobel Prize, 34
North America, 43

NSAIDs, 36
nuclear genome, 77
nucleus, 102
nutraceutical, vii, ix, 41, 42, 43, 48, 58, 60
nutrients, 55
nutrition, 62, 74

O

oil, 42, 58, 59
old age, 17
oligomers, 16
oligosaccharide, 36
opportunities, 24
organ(s), ix, 10, 13, 16, 17, 18, 19, 21, 30, 35, 38, 53
organism, 57
orthostatic hypotension, 17
oxalate, ix, 71, 74, 99, 101
oxidation, 57
oxidative stress, 57
oxygen, 48

P

parallel, x, 72, 83, 93, 97, 100
paraprotein, vii, 2, 3, 19
paraproteinaemias, vii, 2
pasta, 43, 50, 61, 62
pathogenesis, viii, 2, 3, 15, 18, 19, 20, 28
pathogens, 3, 55
pathology, 23
pathways, x, 72, 75, 78
PCR, 56
pepsin, 83
peptide(s), ix, x, 42, 47, 51, 53, 54, 55, 56, 57, 58, 61, 62, 63, 64, 65, 66, 67, 68, 6972, 83, 84, 95
perforation, 30
peripheral blood, 12
peripheral neuropathy, 17, 18
permeability, 35
permit, 3
pH, 45, 61

phagocytosis, 6
pharmaceutical, 59
pharmacology, 52
phenolic compounds, 58
phenotype, 9
phosphorus, 42
phosphorylation, 8, 22
physical properties, 10
physicians, 21
physicochemical properties, 47, 64
phytosterols, 57
placenta, 6
placental barrier, 33
plants, x, 43, 44, 45, 46, 47, 48, 55, 64, 68, 71, 77, 78, 100
plasma cells, vii, viii, 1, 2, 3, 5, 8, 9, 10, 13, 15, 18, 21, 29, 30, 35
plasma proteins, vii, viii, 29, 30
plastid, 102
platelets, 35
polymers, 16
polypeptide(s), vii, 2, 3, 5, 44, 45, 50, 51, 84, 85, 86, 87, 89, 94, 104
polyphenols, 57, 58
polysaccharide, 36
population, 10, 19, 23, 34, 42, 48, 55
positive feedback, 22
poverty, 42
precipitation, 42
pregnancy, 12
preparation, 42, 65, 97
president, 30
prevention, viii, 2, 16, 54
priming, 52, 62
principles, 52
probe, 84
prognosis, viii, 2, 3, 14, 20, 21
prokaryotic cell, 46
proliferation, vii, ix, 2, 9, 42, 51, 52, 64, 70
propranolol, 53
protease globulins, vii, viii, 29, 30
protection, 3, 34, 82
protein engineering, 48
protein hydrolysates, 49, 54, 57, 62, 67
protein sequence, 45

protein structure, 45, 98, 99, 100, 104
proteinase, 81, 83, 94, 95, 98, 99
proteins, vii, ix, x, 1, 3, 4, 7, 9, 10, 12, 16, 24, 25, 32, 34, 41, 43, 44, 45, 46, 48, 49, 50, 51, 52, 54, 55, 56, 57, 60, 61, 62, 63, 64, 65, 66, 68, 69, 72, 74, 77, 79, 82, 93, 99, 100, 101, 102, 103, 104
proteinuria, 20
proteolysis, x, 17, 49, 54, 62, 69, 72, 76, 81, 82, 83, 84, 85, 86, 87, 88, 89, 90, 91, 93, 94, 95, 96, 97, 98, 99, 100, 102, 103, 104
proteolytic enzyme, 103
proteome, 25, 102
proteomics, 45, 70
public health, 53
pulp, ix, 30, 37, 38
purification, 46, 47, 56, 60, 63, 67, 69, 85

Q

quantification, 13, 21, 24

R

radicals, 57
rape, 44
reactant(s), 12, 13
reaction time, 83, 84, 85, 89, 90, 93, 96
reactions, 34, 36, 83
reactive oxygen, 57
reactivity, 18, 38
reagents, 13
receptors, 3, 30, 34, 35, 38, 53
recognition, 21, 32
recombinant proteins, 46, 55, 60
recombinases, 7
recombination, 3, 5, 7, 22, 23
recommendations, 26
relatives, 102
renal failure, 13, 17, 20, 36
renin, 53, 57
repair, 8
reserves, 82, 100, 103

residues, viii, 29, 31, 34, 54, 76, 81, 82, 86, 88, 98, 99
resistance, 54, 57, 88
resources, 42, 43
response, vii, viii, 1, 9, 10, 17, 19, 21, 24, 26, 29, 30, 33, 38, 51, 63
responsiveness, 14, 18, 19
restenosis, 54
reticulum, 66
RH, 26
rhinitis, 35
rings, 44
risk, 10, 14, 16, 23, 24, 25, 26, 34, 36, 39, 51, 62
risk factors, 14, 15, 23
risk management, 36
rituximab, 19
RNA, 22
routes, 35
Royal Society, 23
rubber, 36

S

safety, 54
salt soluble proteins, ix, 41
SAP, 16
scatter, 13
scavengers, 57
sclerosis, 59
SDS-PAGE, 47, 84, 85, 87, 88, 89, 96
secrete, 5, 9
secretion, vii, 2, 3, 52
sedentary lifestyle, 52
sedimentation, 44
seed, vii, ix, x, 41, 43, 45, 46, 47, 48, 59, 60, 61, 62, 64, 65, 66, 67, 68, 69, 71, 72, 74, 75, 77, 78, 79, 80, 82, 84, 99, 100, 101, 102, 103, 104
seed storage proteins, ix, 41, 43, 68, 74, 102
seedlings, 72
sensitivity, 21
sensitization, 6, 35, 38
sequencing, 84, 88
serine, 8

serum, vii, viii, 1, 2, 6, 9, 10, 12, 13, 14, 16, 17, 18, 19, 20, 21, 24, 26, 27, 29, 30, 32, 33
serum immunofixation, 13
shape, 10
sheep, 60
shellfish, 36
shock, ix, 30, 35, 38
showing, ix, 42
side chain, 84
side effects, 53
signal transduction, 34
signs, 17
simulation, 58
sinuses, ix, 30, 36, 38
skin, 53, 59
smooth muscle, 57
smooth muscle cells, 54, 65
society, 52
sodium, 36
software, 102
solubility, 44, 45, 49, 68
solution, 36
somatic mutations, 18, 26
South America, 43
soybeans, 100
species, 43, 44, 57, 77, 83, 92, 100
spermatophytes, ix, 71, 72, 74, 79, 102
spleen, ix, 30, 38
splenomegaly, 18
spore, 100, 101
stability, 23, 45, 72, 80, 91, 99, 100
starch, 65
state(s), 16, 59, 99
statistics, 23
steel, 30, 31
steroids, 42
stimulation, 5, 6, 21
stimulus, 4
stomach, 59
storage, vii, ix, x, 41, 43, 45, 46, 48, 56, 62, 65, 68, 71, 72, 73, 74, 75, 76, 77, 78, 79, 80, 81, 82, 83, 99, 100, 101, 102, 103
stratification, 14, 21, 24, 26
stress, 69

stroke, 52
stromal cells, 16
structural characteristics, 49
structural modifications, 62
structure, vii, viii, 3, 29, 30, 31, 33, 39, 44,
    47, 48, 49, 59, 68, 73, 74, 76, 77, 79, 80,
    82, 85, 86, 87, 88, 89, 91, 92, 93, 94, 95,
    99, 100, 101, 103
substrate, x, 72, 82, 90, 99, 100
sulfur, 44
Sun, 63
suppression, 20, 24
surface area, 98, 99
survival, 17, 18, 20, 26
susceptibility, x, 72, 88, 91, 95, 97, 99
suspensions, 55
sustainability, 68
swelling, 16
symptoms, 10, 17, 51
synapse, 7
syndrome, 8, 16, 18, 22, 27, 36, 63
synthesis, 47, 51, 72, 104

T

T cell, ix, 42, 52, 62
tandem repeats, 55
target, 15, 25, 47
taxa, 74, 77
T-cell receptor, 30
TCR, 6, 30
techniques, 45, 46
technology, 21
temperature, 48, 50
texture, 49
therapeutic agents, 53
therapy, 12, 17, 20, 68
thermal stability, 48
thermal treatment, 49, 68
thyroid, 12
tissue, 16, 17, 19, 35
tobacco, 47, 62, 69
total cholesterol, 58
toxin, 3, 30
transferrin, 12

transformation, 20, 51, 69
transgene, 56
translocation, 21
transplantation, 15
treatment, viii, 2, 3, 10, 14, 15, 17, 18, 19,
    20, 21, 24, 25, 26, 35, 36, 48, 53, 54, 55
treatment agents, 15
triggers, 83, 91, 100
trypsin, 49, 57, 62, 83, 85, 88, 94, 95, 96,
    98, 103
tryptophan, 44
tumor(s), 15, 17, 19, 25, 51
tumor cells, 51
tyrosine, 34, 64

U

UK, 22, 68
uniform, 26, 55
United Nations, 62
United States, 9, 34
urine, vii, viii, 2, 9, 10, 14, 17, 18, 20, 21,
    23, 24
urticaria, 35

V

vaccines, viii, 2, 36
variables, 44
variations, 21
varieties, 43, 59, 61, 62
vasculitis, 18
vasodilator, 53
vegetables, 36, 42
vehicles, 55
viruses, 55
viscoelastic properties, 50
viscosity, 50
vitamins, 57

W

water, 12, 42, 49, 50, 52, 64
Western blot, 56

World Health Organization (WHO), 18, 45,
    62
worldwide, 21

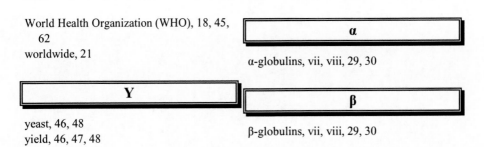

α-globulins, vii, viii, 29, 30

yeast, 46, 48
yield, 46, 47, 48

β-globulins, vii, viii, 29, 30